To MY DEAREST BEVERLEY
A LIFETIME FRIEND
ALLWAYS & FOREVER
ALL MY LOVE
FROM
BOB   X X X

FRED DIBNAH'S CHIMNEY DROPS

WILLIAM HEDLEY'S "PUFFING BILLY"

SHANKS' RETURN TUBE VERTICAL
BOILER AND VERTICAL ENGINE

THOMSON ROAD STEAMER

THE LANCASHIRE BOILER

Alan McEwen

****

WORLD FROM ROUGH STONES HOUSE,
COWLING, KEIGHLEY, WEST YORKSHIRE, BD22 0NW

SLEDGEHAMMER ENGINEERING PRESS LTD

**DEDICATED TO THE MEMORY
OF MY CLOSE FRIEND AND FELLOW LANCASTRIAN
MASTER STEEPLEJACK
DR. FRED DIBNAH M.B.E.**

ACKNOWLEDGEMENTS

Chris Hill; Stan Davies; Sue Gould; Peter Foy; Anthony Green; Stan Holt; Andrew Chorley; Ray Willoughby; John Ellison; Gordon Connolly; Stanley Challenger Graham; Mike Rothwell; A. Drabble; Gordon Moore; Angela B. Horrigan; Ian Thompson; David Devine; Daniel Meadows.

Leigh Library, Local History Officer – Tom Ashcroft;
Touchstone Rochdale. Local Studies Officer – Julian Jefferson;
Caroline Furey, Bolton Museum and Archive Service;
Catherine Smythe, News Editor, Rossendale Free Press;
John Simpson, Helmshore Local History Society;
Margaret Koppens, Halliwell Local History Society;
Jennifer Clark, Local Studies Assistant, Oldham Local Studies & Archives;
Blackburn with Darwen Library;
Lynn Ashwell, Deputy Editor, Bolton News;
Dave Appleton, Editor, Rochdale Observer;
Katherine Walsh, Accrington Library;
Tim Ashurst, Eccles Library;
Terry J. Almond, Heritage Centre Horwich;
Alex Miller, Wigan Archives Service;
Danny Cleary, Lancashire Telegraph,
Katherine Lynn, Bolton News Library;
Jim Francis (Turton Local History Society).

SPECIAL THANKS TO:

Mrs. Sheila Dibnah, (Widow of Fred Dibnah); Paul Donoghue, (Rallyscene Ltd); Phillip Hirst, M.D. (Oldham Evening Chronicle); Harry Forshaw, (Forshaws Demolition Ltd); Bill Partington, (Builder and Poet); Julie Daley, (Atherton & Tyldesley Directory); Mick Berry; Neil Carney; Eddie Chattwood. (Fred's trusted assistants); Jackie Nolan; John Phillp, (Northern Mill Engine Society).

And finally to my wife Christine, for without her, this book would not have been achieved.

My sincerest apologies to anyone I have not included.

ABOUT THE AUTHOR

Alan is an enthusiastic researcher, writer and photographer of industrial history which has fascinated him from being a youngster. When he was just 14 years old, Alan researched and produced a small booklet titled, 'THE HOPWOOD COLLIERY WAGGONWAY'. Regrettably it has been out of print for over 40 years.

In 1977, he researched, wrote and published, 'COLLECTING QUACK CURES', and in 1998 wrote 'CHRONICLES OF A LANCASTRIAN BOILERMAKER', his autobiography relating his passionate story of how, after serving an apprenticeship as a boilermaker, he became Managing Director and Chief Engineer of nationally renowned industrial and heritage boiler engineers, H.A. McEWEN (BOILER REPAIRS) LIMITED, the family firm that he had founded in 1968. Alan retired from the company in November 2007, handing over the reins of the firm that was his life for almost four decades, to his son Alasdair. He still acts as consultant engineer to his old firm when required.

Alan has also written numerous articles for magazines and books about British Industrial Heritage; he has been a member of the Newcomen Society for over 25 years and the Northern Mill Engine Society for around 20 years. He is currently in the throes of researching and writing another book to be titled: 'LANCASHIRE AND YORKSHIRE MILLTOWN DISASTERS'. To be published by Sledgehammer Engineering Press Ltd, late 2009.

Alan is a keen collector of railwayana and makers' plates from steam engines, boilers and old textile machinery.

Also by Sledgehammer Engineering Press:
Chronicles of a Lancastrian Boilermaker, 1998. ***ISBN: 0-9532725-0-8***

Forthcoming new titles:
Lancashire and Yorkshire Milltown Disasters by Alan McEwen, late 2009.

Smokestacks – An Illustrated History Of Industrial Chimneys In Northern England And The Industries They Served, by Alan McEwen, 2010.

Jaggermen's Bridges on Packhorse Trails, by Christine McEwen, 2009.

Published by Sledgehammer Engineering Press Ltd, World From Rough Stones House, Farling Top, Cowling, Keighley, West Yorkshire, BD22 0NW, England,
Telephone: 01535 637153   Email: lankyboilermaker@btconnect.com

All distribution enquiries should be addressed to the publisher.

Printed by Amadeus Press, Ezra House, West 26 Business Park, Cleckheaton, West Yorkshire, BD19 4TQ
Telephone: 01274 863210: Fax: 01274 863211: Email: info@ amadeuspress.co.uk Website: amadeuspress.co.uk

FRED'S OWN MINIATURE MILL CHIMNEY
©Alan McEwen Industrial Heritage Collection

Back in the early spring of 1992 on a sunlit, pleasant evening I called at Fred's yard as I oftimes did every fortnight or so. On entering the yard, I didn't see Fred at all, but I could make out the distinct sounds of a pick axe striking hard ground coming from the rear of Fred's Dank's horizontal steam boiler.

Venturing over, I could see my mate, Fred wielding the pick axe, cutting into the hard surface of the yard, comprising a mixture of old ashes and gravel.

After we moved on from the usual friendly greetings, on me asking Fred what the excavations were about, he cheerfully and enthusiastically informed me that his aim was to fill a longtime ambition: he was going to build 'a magnificent mill chimney in miniature', was how he described in great detail the construction of the beautiful square brick chimney which rises to a height of 45 feet that Fred has bestowed as a legacy to the mill chimney builders art.

During another evening's visit, I actually assisted Fred in manoeuvring and laying some monster-sized flagstones that he had collected from a local cotton mill, to act as the foundation for the chimney.

Working on the building of the chimney when he had the odd bit of spare time actually took him eight years to complete.

On the 3rd February 2000 the BBC filmed Fred and his wife Sheila celebrating the completion of the chimney whilst proudly ensconced high on the chimney top, both enjoying a champagne and smoked salmon lunch. Fred was extremely proud of his creation and placed a plaque midway up the stack inscribed with his initials F.D. and the date of completion.

When I complimented him on his beautiful and graceful creation, he jovially said, "Eeh Alan, as well as you will remember, the chimneys were like blades of grass – they were all over the place. But there ain't many now, and as you know I've personally dropped a fair number of chimneys in me time, but surprisingly I've not built too many. I've been some eight years building me little stack which I have done in dribs and drabs whenever I had a bit of spare time I worked on it. But in recent years I have hardly any bloody spare time, so that's why it's took me so long. Mind you, it's probably the very last chimney to be built in Bolton".

Chimney Materials
The bricks came from a wide variety of local sources. The ornate oversiller, Fred cast from concrete down on the ground; the moulds were made from old plastic chemical drums and plywood. On completion he hauled the heavy ornamental oversiller up to the chimney top with chain-blocks. Fred's chimney is undoubtedly a testament to his unrivalled steeplejacking knowledge, his practical skills and also to the chimney builders of the Victorian era.

INTRODUCTION

FRED DIBNAH MASTER STEEPLEJACK AND CHIMNEY FELLER

Fred Dibnah and the author in Fred's Engine Shed. For over 20 years Fred, Master Steeplejack and expert chimney feller, would often relate to Alan dramatic stories of steeplejacking lore and particularly chimney drops in either the Engine Shed or the 'hen-hut' workshop.
©Alan McEwen Industrial Heritage Collection

Nationally renowned Master Steeplejack, Fred Dibnah was born on the 29th April 1938 in the Lancashire cotton town of Bolton. Even as a young lad, Fred was considered by his family and also his contemporaries as being a little odd, rather eccentric, for the young Boltonian eschewed the normal football and similar sports–related pastimes in favour of the world of steam engines, boilers and in particular the numerous cotton mill and factory chimneys that were as ubiquitous as blades of grass. For the young Fred Dibnah was captivated by the gigantic, gleaming steam engines with their enormous whirling flywheels that powered the cotton mills and that were jammed cheek by jowl into Bolton's townscape. Fred also had a profound interest in the many classes of steam locomotives that regularly clanked by close to his boyhood home in Burden Park, and he regularly visited Bolton Loco Depot, where he would spend hour upon hour, fascinated, watching and studying the various steam shunting locomotives and goods engines stabled at the sheds. Fred clearly loved all aspects of British industry and was fascinated by the numerous ancient coal pits with their distinctive headgear that he saw when taking a regular walk along the towpath of the Manchester, Bury and Bolton Canal. Indeed, many years later when he became famous, he would delight his audiences with his colourful reminiscences and adventures regarding the Lancashire coalmining industry.

Fred's greatest passion however, was industrial chimneys and steeplejacking, which had thrilled him from being a small lad when he had witnessed, during the local wakes weeks when the cotton mills closed, the sight of steeplejack's' red-painted ladders running up the sides of the towering mill chimneys and the tiny 'Lowry-esq' figures, the steeplejacks 'dancing around' on the platform some 200 feet up in the sky.

By the early 1960s the cotton industry and its ancillary trades were in a severe downward spiral of decline. The demise of this once prominent industry (in the nineteenth century the boast of Lancashire's millowners was: 'England's bread was won by Lancashire's thread'), was excellent at first for the young Fred Dibnah whose ambition and most fervent desire was to become established as a steeplejack. The numerous mill and other industrial chimneys scattered all over Bolton and the other neighbouring Lancashire cotton towns all radiating out from the hub: (Manchester, known as the cottonopolis), which for decades had been beautifully engineered and subsequently regularly repaired, would from now on require to be demolished. Fred regarded these mill chimneys as monuments to the industrial age. He held these towering structures with great affection and he often related stories about the 'hard men', the chimney builders who erected them and of the men also, who maintained and repaired them: the steeplejacks. As Fred eloquently put it, "these chimneys had served their masters well; they were no longer loved and had therefore to be done away with: demolished". But to just place an explosive charge in the chimney's base and blow them down when they came to the end of their lives, did not appeal to Fred, for to him there was another more traditional way of felling these chimneys that embodied respect for the old time chimney builders – and would demolish them with great aplomb and not a little drama.

Fred Dibnah's procedure for carrying out a chimney felling was the result of a well considered demolition plan, based on traditional Victorian practice known in steeplejacking parlance as 'gobbing out and pit-propping'. Fred termed it as 'the science of back'ards construction'.

By the employment of this tried and tested procedure, Fred almost made it into an art, because from the early 1970s his fame as an expert chimney feller became renowned. His deep-seated knowledge of chimney construction and of steeplejacking lore, his charismatic and competent showmanship rapidly made him nationally famous: particularly following those memorable early BBC television programmes. His name became synonymous with the stereo type no-nonsense, straight-talking Northern character, and of craftsmanship, hard graft and of daring-do.

Fred's later television series particularly made his character blossom, his passionate and oftimes comical descriptions of how the complexities of historic mechanical wizardry were built and how they operated, thrilled his television audiences nationally. He was a most brilliant, natural speaker, and especially gifted in being able to 'paint a picture' in his distinctive Boltonian accent. Fred was awarded two honourary degrees: the first was from The Robert Gordon Institute of Technology, Aberdeen, and the second from The University of Birmingham. Thereafter, he was Doctor Fred Dibnah. In July 2004, Fred was awarded the M.B.E. for services to television and broadcasting. On the 6th November 2004, Fred died after bravely battling with bladder cancer since autumn of 2001.

FRED'S GOBBING OUT AND PIT-PROPPING PROCEDURE

With Fred having carefully planned the direction of the condemned chimney's fall which he termed 'the drop zone', the gobbing out would then be started by him and his men cutting a slot into the side of the chimney and the removal of the loose bricks or stonework. This slot would be around three feet high by a width of around eighteen inches.

The most dramatic of Fred's chimney demolition jobs were the chimneys that had to be felled by chopping a hole through the base in the direction of the planned fall. This is known as 'gobbing out'. As the gob was cut through the base brick work of the chimney which could be considerable in thickness, timber props, known as 'pit-props' and sawn from short sections of old timber telegraph and electricity poles would be inserted into the gobbed openings with 'cap-pieces', sections cut from old wooden nine inch by three inch planks placed on top. Long, thin tapered wedges cut from oak, ash or other hardwoods would then be firmly driven between the top of the 'cap-pieces' and the underside brick work of the 'gob', thus producing stout and immensely strong supports for the massive weight of masonry towering above.

This procedure was repeated around the circumference of the chimney base until approximately one third had been gobbed and pit-propped. This would result in, as Fred put it, "the thing feeling the pain". This meant that the tall structure was now balanced on the numerous pit-props and was therefore ready for the stacking of the demolition bonfire.

During Fred's long career of steeplejacking which spanned some forty years he was instrumental in demolishing ninety cotton mill and factory chimneys. His last one Park No. 2 Mill, Royton he carried out six months before he died in November 2004. Many of these chimney demolition jobs were carried out brick by brick, which commenced by Fred having to fasten his distinctive red-painted wooden ladders up the side of the chimney until he reached the top which could have been 200 to 300 feet above the ground. Once the top was attained, he would then construct his working platforms from steel scaffolding poles, timber battens and long, nine inch wide planks.

Once completed, this working platform would allow Fred the often arduous and profoundly dangerous task of removing the cap-stones, many being hugely hewn stone blocks that formed the chimney cap and wide oversillers. He would commence by cautiously cutting through the angle irons, iron or steel bars to allow the dismantling to take place. Fred often said that this dangerous procedure had caused the death of numerous steeplejacks, because as they cut through the iron work which tightly held the stone work together, very similar to a giant clamp, everything thus being held in tension; as soon as the iron was cut through the whole of the chimney top could suddenly spring forth and disintegrate, resulting in the destruction of the steeplejack's working platforms, and on many occasions causing the men to be thrown off to fall to their deaths.

Most steeplejacks tackled the demolition work in teams of two, three or more. Fred demolished oversillers and truncated numerous tall and profoundly structurally dangerous chimneys, removing many of them totally by himself. Obviously playing a useful and profoundly reliable job on the ground, would be Fred's assistants who would haul up, by the use of a mixture of pulleywheels and ropes, the ladders, iron dogs, scaffolding poles, timber battens, planks etc, as Fred required them. These stalwarts would lower to the ground, hundreds of tons of brick and masonry in the ingenious rope-worked metal cylinders known as 'Fred's Flying Buckets'. Even though Fred was undoubtedly an expert Master Steeplejack, he couldn't have managed without the skills of his long-time, well respected mates such as Donald Payton, Mick Berry and Neil Carney. Fred was also ably assisted on numerous jobs by fellow steeplejack Eddie Chattwood for well over 35 years.

FRED'S PROCEDURES FOR THE DEMOLITION OF CHIMNEYS

1. Timber 'Sole pieces' 9" x 3" to be placed on bottom of 'gobbed out' opening cut through brickwork or stonework.

2. Timber 'Cap pieces' 9" x 3" to be placed on the top of the 'pit-props'.

3. Hardwood Wedges – usually sawn in Fred's workshop by steam powered saw. These long, thinly tapering wedges are driven beneath the 'cap pieces' and on top of the 'pit-props'. One wedge is placed at the front, the other at the rear. Both are driven in by hammering simultaneously to create optimum tightening of the 'pit-prop' supports.

4. 'Pit-props' – sawn to the required length from old telegraph poles and to have square-cut ends.

5. 'Gobbed-out' – This refers to the hole cut through the chimney wall to weaken the structure. The 'pit-props' are placed inside the 'gob' or 'mouth' to support the chimney mass.

6. 'Mouth' – Another word – as above.

7. Trammel Points are an adjustable tool comprising two separate steel points that can slide along a steel bar which assists Fred to take accurate measurements on a vertical plane of the chimney masonry opposite the 'gobbed-out' section; particularly important on square-base chimneys. Accuracy with these measurements assist in plotting the path of the chimney drop zone. The procedure is that Fred would paint a horizontal and a vertical line in white paint to the rear of the 'gob'; equally above and beneath the horizontal line and on the vertical centre line he would drill one small hole into the masonry. Fred would then place the top trammel point in the top hole, and the bottom point would then be engaged in the bottom hole. The points would then be tightened up by thumbing knurled screws. The trammel points were thus set which recorded the exact distance prior to the bonfire weakening the supporting 'pit-props'.

As a consequence of the 'pit-props' gradually becoming weak due to the ravaging effects of the fire, the chimney would generally then commence pressing down on the supports, and this movement could be detected with the trammel points.

FRED's QUOTES

1. Did yer like that?

2. The modern world stinks.

3. I'm just a bum who climbs chimneys.

4. One mistake up here, and it's half a day out with the undertaker.

5. I set out as a steeplejack in my youth to preserve chimneys. I've finished up knocking most of them down.

6. Fred commenced his chimney demolition career by applying what he called, "the science of back'ards construction".

7. "Once the fire is lit, it's out of your hands; it's in the hands of 'The Man in the Sky' ".

8. "You've always got the twenty minutes of dry-throated inaction until the thing feels the action of the fire".

9. "I sometimes get characters coming out of the crowd following a drop and ask me if I ever worry. I usually tell them that I always worry until the thing is safely on the deck, and it'd take a bloody brave man to tackle a large chimney with a box o'matches and not worry!"

10. "After the usual chimney drop, I get all sorts of folk approach me, each carrying a red-hot brick for me to sign my autograph on".

11. "When you're up on the top of the staging around a 200 foot tall chimney, should you make a wrong move causing you to fall, then it's half a day out with the undertaker".

FRED DIBNAH'S CHIMNEY DROPS
CONTENTS

CALEB WRIGHT'S MILL CHIMNEY DEMOLITION, TYLDESLEY, NR. WIGAN.

March 1970

An undated aerial picture depicting the extensive Caleb Wright's Mill in the centre foreground, part of the Barnfield complex and fronted by the diagonally running and aptly named Shuttle Street. Largest of several cotton mills in the town, it provided employment to many along with Chanters Colliery, located immediately above the central and left hand chimneys.
Copyright: Wigan Archives Service WLCT

Back in the early 1990s, Fred and I were contentedly ensconced on a couple of horsehair upholstered chairs inside my Farling Top Steam Engine House museum, each enjoying a glass of cool, Yorkshire bitter as he dramatically entertained me with the following story:

Caleb Wright's Mill photographed from Shuttle Street May 1992.
Copyright: Wigan Archives Service WLCT

Fred's Story:

"Around twenty odd years ago, I think it were 1970, early in the year, maybe March because it were freezing cold, Courtaulds, one of my best customers gave me the job of demolishing a massive 200 foot chimney at a mill of their's in Tyldesley called Caleb Wright's Mill. There were actually two mill chimneys, one were still active, but because this particular chimney I were gonna drop were hemmed in on all sides by other buildings and close also to lots of nearby-houses, the Courtaulds management wouldn't let me gob it out and drop it by my bumfire procedure. Therefore, I had to knock it down brick by brick, which were a bloody big job. That night at home, I rang a good mate of mine, Kenneth who liked working with me on chimneys, but were actually a very good violinist and a member of the Hallé Orchestra in Manchester. Kenneth jumped at the chance of working on such a big chimney and instead of practising for a forthcoming concert in the Free Trade Hall in Manchester, he came and assisted me in laddering the chimney to the top."

Fred and Kenneth perch precariously on top of the tall brick stack during the demolition of Caleb Wright's Mill chimney.
Paul Donoghue Collection

FRED DIBNAH'S CHIMNEY DROPS

"This Caleb Wright's chimney weren't that old really for a tall mill chimney. A chap told me it had been built around 1900, it were seventy years old therefore. The chimney had been built at the same time as the huge mill by a local firm called Robert Gregson. Back in 1844 this local entrepreneur, Caleb Wright established himself as a cotton spinner and he commenced by building Barnfield Mills, on what were then green fields. Caleb had been born in 1820, one of a family of thirteen. He died in 1898. The big modern mill were named Caleb Wright's Mill and dominated the town."

"Not only were it perishing cold, it were reet windy too and causing the chimney to sway like a ship in a storm. After erecting the staging, we got stuck in with relish and demolished the cap which were made of big sections of stone and then carried on knocking off row after row of bricks until we managed to reduce the chimney by around fifty feet. However, things thereafter got reet difficult. We found the bricks suddenly became really hard like, and the mortar too became harder as we progressed downwards. I've often said that the chimney builders of old must have known a trick or two that us modern steeplejacks do not know. Kenneth were a clever chap with plenty of the grey matter and were as keen as me in fettling the job. He were that interested that he abandoned his violin practice just to stay and help me. I were most grateful too."

"We got quite desperate and in the hope of breaking out the brickwork faster, we hauled up a large jackhammer, you know those that navvies use on road mending jobs. It were reet unsteady attempting to operate the bloody thing being so high up and deadly too. But despite much effort, we had to abandon the idea. We tried all sorts of different devices, you know, of the 'Heath Robinson' type, just to cut out the bricks."

"I were getting more and more troubled, the job were taking a hell of a lot longer than I had allowed for in my quotation to Courtaulds and the weeks were flying by. Kenneth and I put our heads together. He came up with the idea of placing small explosive devices within the brickwork, but my customer wouldn't allow explosives on the mill site. We then improvised several versions of brick-wrecking machines using large screw jacks, but still we weren't reducing the chimney's height fast enough."

"One new morning, full of fresh ideas, we decided that we'd tackle the chimney from the inside by reducing the thickness, so we began chiselling the brickwork from around the internal circumference. We found that these inside bricks, seemed a lot less hard than the external ones, and so we progressed better. Suddenly, without any warning, disaster struck. The bloody stubborn chimney that had given us both so much grief, without warning, suddenly split down the middle. We were very lucky that it didn't collapse onto us. After getting out of the chimney and examining the crack, which were still travelling we were just about to step well away as this would enable us to inspect the fabric of the chimney all around, when there were a loud bang sort of noise. The next second, a massive four feet cube of brickwork fell inside the base where we had been previously working. This were quickly followed by another huge lump, but twice as big which danced off the left hand side of the stack and plummeted right through the nearby roof of the mill's Blacksmith's shop, which made me shudder. We both jumped down and headed, white-faced towards the Blacksmith's shop which now had a gigantic hole where the roof used to be. Fortunately, thanks to the 'Man in the Sky', but there were no dead bodies or even injured blokes to greet us. The massive brick lump had smashed the main line shaft putting a number of the machines out of action. Hell's Teeth! My career in steeplejacking is in ruins, I thought."

Caleb Wright's Mill chimney base showing the huge mound of bricks that Fred and Kenneth have dropped down the inside as they reduced the height of the stack brick by brick. The men will have dropped the bricks down the centre of the chimney for them to be discharged onto the mound via the hole that had been cut into the chimney's side, seen to the right hand side of the ladder.
Paul Donoghue Collection

CALEB WRIGHT'S MILL, TYLDESLEY

"I later learned that whilst this destructive force had interfered with our job, the mill's Chief Engineer were enjoying a game of billiards in the works canteen situated on the bottom side of the mill, as was his normal thing during the dinnertime. One of the Blacksmiths raced across the mill yard and entered the canteen to break the bad news. 'Chief, Fred Dibnah's just smashed the Blacksmith's shop', shrieked the young Blacksmith. The mill's Chief Engineer, luckily for us, were one of them old time, cool heroic types just like Sir Francis Drake, you know, the Admiral who were playing bowls whilst the Spanish Armada were bearing down on the English coast. 'Has anyone got killed?' the Chief Engineer mildly inquired whilst still squinting down the length of his billiard's cue. 'No Chief', replied the young Blacksmith. 'Well awreet then lad, thee get back to work, I'll just finish off my game".

An early photograph of the imposing Caleb Wright's Mill and the tall graceful cylindrical chimney. In the foreground of the picture is an unidentified steam traction engine and to the right is a horse-hauled four wheeled cart piled high with goods; to the left of the traction engine are what appear to be two fairground-type trailers; numerous cotton mill operatives dwellings complete this highly atmospheric most typical Lancashire mill town scene.
Copyright: Wigan Archives Service WLCT

"That sodding chimney Alan, were a pig right to the bitter end. As well as employing the 50 ton hydraulic jack, I used my steam roller as well. We lashed a bloody great thick steel cable around the chimney's brickwork and with a full head of steam I would drive away until the lump was shifted, and we just ploughed on pulling off massive lumps of brickwork."

"When we had finally decked that chimney and Caleb Wright's management were satisfied, Kenneth the violinist and me drowned our sorrows in a local pub. Perhaps it was the ten pints of best bitter, but I reckoned that the 'ghosts of the Victorian chimney builders' who had originally built Caleb Wright's Mill chimney were laughing at our efforts."

Fred cheerfully poses for the camera, his weighty 12 pound sledgehammer over his shoulder as he leans onto a huge block of the chimney's brickwork. Shortly after this image was captured by the photographer, this massive and heavy block which is seen here supported by Fred's 50 ton hydraulic jack was suddenly dislodged and fell downwards over thirty feet to crash through the roof of the Blacksmith's shop causing severe damage.
Paul Donoghue Collection

In 1993, some twenty three years after Fred had demolished the tallest of the two mill chimneys at Caleb Wright's Mill, he was invited by the demolition contractors who were engaged on demolishing the whole of Caleb Wright's Mill to quote for the demolition of the remaining chimney.

However, because they considered Fred's price to be too high, the demolition contractors decided to tackle the destruction and removal of the mill chimney themselves which evidently got them into a spot of bother with the good townsfolk of Tyldesley. The story goes that during the demolition process, a large section of the chimney's brickwork suddenly collapsed and fell which resulted in causing some significant damage to the Salvation Army hut which was situated across from the demolition site in Eliott Street. On hearing this story, a builder, Bill Partington from nearby Daisy Hill, Westhoughton spontaneously penned this delightful poem:

CALEB'S TOWER

Fred Dibnah gave them free advice

Because it was so tall.

But they ignored those kindly words,

They thought they knew it all.

Fred shook his head and mopped his

brow,

And said "They're Bloody Barmy!"

So when they pulled those chocks away,

It flattened Sally Army!

By courtesy of the poet, Billy Partington

GREAT LEVER SPINNING MILL CHIMNEY DROP, BOLTON.

A Sunday in 1971

Great Lever Spinning Mill's tall smoke stack with the base gobbed out and propped in readiness for dropping.
Paul Donoghue Collection

The demolition of the Great Lever Spinning Mill chimney was perhaps one of Fred's earliest recorded chimney drops, and I am grateful to Fred's old friend Harry Forshaw of Walter Forshaw Limited demolition contractors for filming the event, and for his kindness in loaning me a copy of the film.

Great Lever Spinning Mill was constructed in 1874 as a six storey rectangular cotton spinning mill and with its attendant brick-built warehouses, offices, boiler and engine house, was typical in design to its contemporary mills. The mill was originally operated by Thomas Taylor & Sons Limited, and was known as Grecian New Mill No. 4, prior to being called the Great Lever Spinning Mill. In 1884, it is recorded that the mill's entire spindleage amounted to 182,000. By 1890 the mills were extended, which made the building one of the largest in the Great Lever district of Bolton. Cotton production finished in September 1965, during the period the mill was operated by the Courtaulds group. It was later used by a company specialising in waste paper processing.

Fred wearing stove-pipe hat and frock coat at the base of the chimney prior to lighting the bonfire.
Paul Donoghue Collection

Great Lever Spinning Mill, by early 1970 was no longer required; the buildings had stood empty for some time and were plagued by vandalism. In 1971 the demolition of the once fine mill block was underway, and by the time Fred Dibnah was invited to demolish the chimney, many of the surrounding buildings had been knocked down and cleared. The 210 feet tall, striking chimney, which for almost a century had dominated the surrounding area, was now left standing all alone surrounded by demolition debris scattered all over the extensive site.

On the Sunday of the demolition of the chimney, already there was a large crowd forming around the outer fringes of the mill site, many attractively dressed in their 'Sunday best' clothes. Young mini-skirted girls, housewives pushing prams, old men in trilby hats smoking pipes, teenagers with shoulder-length hair, bearded, rough-looking, hard-hatted demolition men with cigarettes in their mouths; all could be seen patiently waiting for Fred the Boltonian chimney demolition expert to arrive.

With just one hour left before the lighting of the bonfire at 12 noon, Fred's battered old ex-Army Landover drove onto the mill site in a cloud of petrol fumes. Fred could be seen, climbing out of the vehicle's cab and attired in a bizarre mixture of clothing. On his head, Fred sported a tall, black stove-pipe hat and covering his work-worn jeans was a long black, frock-coat with short tails. He walked over to the distinctive, octagonal brick chimney whose tall, graceful barrel surmounted a square, attractively panelled brick base that extended vertically from a massive foundation of black-hued moulded gritstone.

In these early days of his steeplejacking career, Fred would often appear to his close friends to be slightly embarrassed and perhaps a trifle ill at ease when surrounded with crowds of watchers.

However, unless you knew him very well, you couldn't tell, for he was ever-cheerful and immensely friendly and would smilingly answer any question regarding his steeplejacking pursuits at anytime. He was an exceptionally confident character, who was knowledgeable and passionate in regard to chimneys and steeplejacking generally.

Within a few minutes of him arriving, Fred could be viewed, cheerfully instructing his lusty cohorts to stack the scrap timber and old lorry tyres required for the chimney's funeral pyre in and around the numerous and well-engineered timber supports, the pit-props, cut from old telegraph poles, that Fred had fitted into the gob he had cut out of the three-feet thick masonry to act as supports for the enormous weighty mass of brick and stone rising above which amounted to several hundred tons. The chopping out of the hard brick and particularly so, the massively hewn gritstone foundation blocks to form the mouth-like opening known in steeplejack's parlance as 'the gob', which Fred had achieved the previous week must have been an exceedingly hard task.

With Fred being garbed in his tall stove-pipe hat and ancient black frock-coat, rather bizarre apparel to wear on a demolition site, was our young steeplejack acting the role of a showman to entertain the large crowd of local people and demolition men, or was Fred attempting to emulate his idol, the famous Victorian mechanical and civil engineer, Isambard Kingdom Brunel? My own perception is that Fred was indeed attempting to caricature Brunel, for this extremely gifted man, out of all of the nineteenth century's engineers, was, most definitely Fred's favourite engineer, whom he respected and eloquently spoke of from his earliest days as a steeplejack and 'back-street mechanic' – right throughout his long career spanning some forty years.

A dramatic image: the bonfire is alight and Fred keeps a close watch on how the flames are burning the pit-props.
Paul Donoghue Collection

The tyres are burning furiously as Fred prepares to leap down from the side of the gob.
Paul Donoghue Collection

Dense black smoke pours out from the blazing lorry tyres and rises into the sky as Fred stands at the base keeping a watchful eye on the bonfire.
Paul Donoghue Collection

At the allotted time, bang on the nail of 12 o'clock, Fred's attractive young wife, Alison officiated by lighting the bonfire by her thrusting an improvised blazing torch into the compacted timber and scrap lorry tyres, which soon after with Fred taking control and several buckets filled with diesel oil being thrown onto the stack of burning fuel, the resulting conflagration raged under the pit-props and up into the chimney. Shortly following, with the tyres blazing furiously, massive plumes of thick, black smoke could be viewed issuing out of the tall, chimney's top and blackening the sky. The loud roaring sound of the orange-hued flames racing up the stack, could be easily heard

from several hundred feet away. Sparks and blobs of molten rubber rained down and the stench of burning rubber pervaded the air. The crowd of fascinated onlookers were silent now, all watching and waiting patiently for the moment, not far off, when the ninety-seven year old, all-dominating mill chimney would collapse. In the nearby terraced 'Coronation Street dwellings', watchers could be seen on front doorsteps, sat upon their yard wall tops, or hanging out of upstairs windows. Many watchers, held ancient photographic equipment such as Brownie box cameras, or the Kodak Instamatic models, all serious in capturing the drama on film.

The beautiful Victorian-built Great Lever Spinning Mill chimney in its death throes.
Paul Donoghue Collection

At 12.25 p.m. just twenty five minutes after the bonfire had been lit, the watchers witnessed a sudden dramatic movement in the stricken stack, then the chimney toppled over and quickly fell, hitting the mill yard with an almighty thump. Clouds of dust and black smoke filled the air. A loud cheer rent the air from the watchers followed by much whistling and clapping of hands. The crowd surged forward to surround their hero, Fred, whose face was a smiling picture of happiness and relief; his job now safely over.

Following Fred's chimney drop, a large bright yellow painted, Caterpiller bulldozer effortlessly cleared away the long, sinuous mounds of smoking brick rubble and loaded it into a fleet of waiting demolition contractor's, eight-wheeled tipper lorries. Finally, Fred could be seen clambering amongst the heaps of smashed brick, with smoke swirling around him, searching for the copper lightning conductor which he wanted to add to his collection at home.

Down tumbles the smoke stack, violently striking the mill yard and sending up a massive cloud of dust and smoke.
Paul Donoghue Collection

Left: Portrait of Fred displaying a typical air of cheerfulness and confidence.
Paul Donoghue Collection

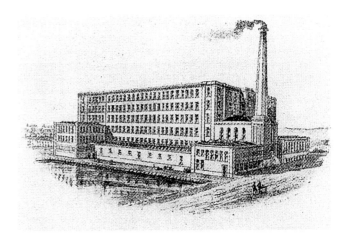

Above: An engraving of Great Lever Spinning Mill taken from an old letterhead.
©Alan McEwen Industrial Heritage Collection

JOHN BRIGHT'S ERA MILL CHIMNEY DROP, WOODBINE STREET, ROCHDALE

Friday 16th March 1979

All in a day's work. Donald looks on as Fred crouching inside the 'gob' chisels out the brickwork; on the outside Mick Berry breaks out the external brickwork.
© Stanley Challenger Graham

Of all of Fred Dibnah's chimney demolition jobs, the one that surely stands out in everyone's mind, is the Era Mill drop. Undoubtedly this is due to the early episodes of Fred's television career, when the BBC's Don Haworth filmed those unforgettable scenes of Fred and his old pal Donald Payton hard at work 'gobbing out' the tall circular brick chimney in absolutely atrocious weather conditions. It was mid March and Fred, Donald and the other stalwart team member Mick Berry battled at the cutting out of the brickwork in the chimney base during a severe snow storm. On the north side of the chimney the film depicts the brickwork thickly covered with a layer of ice, and the viewer can sense with a shiver the unrelenting freezing cold wind blowing down from the nearby Pennine hills, all making Fred's work desperately hard. Nevertheless, the trio battle on, and within four days they had cut a massive gob into around a third of the chimney's circumference and fitted over twenty 'pit-props' and 'cap-pieces' into the three foot high mouth-like opening to support the mass of brickwork towering high above.

On 5th March 1897, the Era Mill Company Limited was formed and for 2d per square yard, purchased the land for constructing the mill on Woodbine Street alongside the Rochdale Canal. The architects who designed the mill and the chimney were Sidney Stott and W. Dixon. Thomas Taylor of Rochdale was awarded the contract to build the mill and the chimney for the sum of £26,150.

The neatly engineered 'gob' displaying the numerous 'pit-props' and 'cap-pieces'. To the left and
right of the chimney's circumference note the thickness of the brickwork.
© Stanley Challenger Graham

Fred, Donald, Mick and several other eager helpers hard at work building the bonfire from old car
and lorry tyres and demolition timber.
© Stanley Challenger Graham

The mill steam engine was built by Petrie & Co., also of Rochdale and was named 'VICTORIA'; it commenced to power the mill on 10 June 1898. Petrie's also built the four, 30 feet long by 9 feet diameter Lancashire boilers.

Just like countless other individuals I was always particularly fascinated by this relatively early but exceedingly well documented example of Fred's chimney drops, and I got Fred to tell me the following story.

Fred's Story:

"This were one hell of a freezing cold job Al. I always found working in Rochdale in winter, far colder than down in Bolton. It's all them high Pennine hills like. The wind blows over from Yorkshire about 350 days of the year and it either rains or snows for about ten months as well. Anyway after me, Donald and Mick had completed the 'gobbing out' and 'pit-propping' on the morning of the drop, which were on a Friday, we then formed the usual bumfire which we built from a huge pile of old wood and dozens of knackered tyres. I like using tyres even though they create a lot of terrible black clag, because they cause the pit-props to burn away faster".

Fred had told me that there were actually two mill chimneys sited quite close together. Era Mill's chimney was the tallest, the other chimney was much shorter and had served the boilerhouse belonging to Moss Mill. He actually dropped both chimneys, commencing with Era Mill and charged the demolition contractor, his close friend Harry Forshaw £500 for Era Mill and £400 for the smaller, Moss Mill stack.

"The powers that be were reet worried that I might drop the tall Era Mill chimney in the Rochdale Canal which were close. But I told them that the mill yard were easily large enough to accommodate the safe dropping of both chimneys and they had nowt to worry about", said Fred laconically.

"Anyway on the Sunday morning, the weather had improved and was much kinder, the snow storm had buggered off and the wind, that terrible freezing, biting wind had stopped blowing. I got Alison to light the bumfire at 12 noon, and after about 20 minutes, down the chimney fell with a great crash which made a reet bloody spread int' mill yard. I'd decided to watch the actual drop from behind a massive steel scrap skip which was placed quite a bit too close to the chimney's drop zone. Hell's Teeth, when the bugger hit the deck, a massive shower of large bricks flew over the top of this 'ere skip just like bloody mortar bombs, whilst others peppered the other side like machine gun bullets. It certainly got the adrenalin flowing. Exciting stuff!."

With cigarette firmly clamped between his lips, Fred makes room for more bonfire materials at the extreme end of the gob by clearing away several heavy steel girders.
© *Stanley Challenger Graham*

Fred's distinctive striped woollen coat together with his bulb air-horn hang from a steel pipe driven into the base of the chimney's brickwork.
© *Stanley Challenger Graham*

John Bright's tall Era Mill chimney and the shorter Moss Mill chimney are dramatically reflected in the still waters of the adjacent Rochdale Canal. The mill buildings stand with sightless windows awaiting their destruction.
© Stanley Challenger Graham

"Just after the drop, I remember saying to Mick who walked past me to collect the copper lightning conductor, 'DID YER LIKE THAT?' – and it has sort of stuck with me ever since. We dropped that big chimney in the right shop. I had

every confidence in how we'd engineered it."
Within the following few days Fred and his team then carried out the equally successful demolition of Moss Mill's chimney

Mick Berry lights the bonfire ignition torch held by Fred whilst Donald and Fred's wife Alison looks on. A television cameraman and a sound engineer record the event which would eventually be watched by millions of Fred fans on T.V.
© Stanley Challenger Graham

Fred, together with two more brave souls, dodge flying bricks whilst crouched behind large steel scrapmetal skips as the Era Mill chimney strikes the mill yard with tremendous violence.
© Stanley Challenger Graham

This photograph taken in a long, dark back street alley or ginnel depicts the Era Mill chimney as it commences its fall to the ground.
Courtesy of Daniel Meadows.

Jubilation! Fred proudly poses on the mass of fallen brickwork.
Courtesy of Daniel Meadows

The Moss Mill chimney now stands all alone; a long sinuous heap of crushed, sooty brickwork is all that remains of the Era Mill chimney. Fred's next job was the successful demolition of the Moss Mill chimney.
© Stanley Challenger Graham

W.R. Pickup Limited
Pearl Brook Fireclay Works,
Horwich, Bolton.
Thursday 27th September 1979

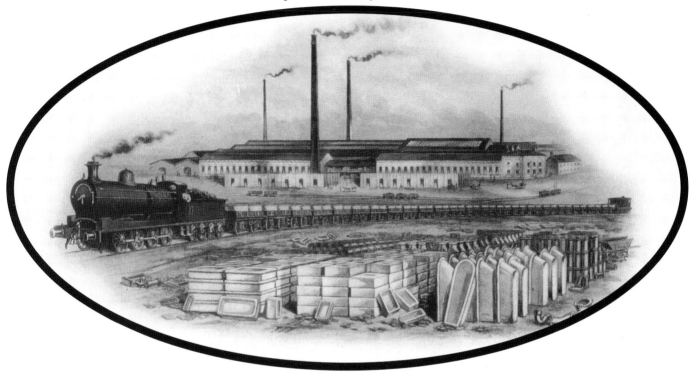

An early 20th century photograph depicting the extensive Pearl Brook Fireclay Works of W.R. Pickup Limited, Horwich.
Photo: Horwich Heritage Centre Collection

The renowned Horwich fireclay products firm of W.R. Pickup Limited was established in 1890, and were nationally acclaimed manufacturers of enamelled fired stoneware: for example, urinals, sinks, lavatories, closets etc. for both domestic and local government buildings, factories etc. Pickups became one of the largest fireclay product manufacturing companies in Britain. Their registered trademark: 'STONITE' was either impressed or transfer-printed onto the firm's wares. Later the firm would become famous for refractory brick products which were in constant demand by numerous iron foundries and steel works all over Britain.

The basic material used in the manufacture of W.R. Pickup's refractory products was fireclay which had been extracted from seams of between four inches and eight inches thick in deep fireclay mines on nearby Winter Hill, the dominant 1500 feet Pennine hillside that rises above Horwich to overlook the town.

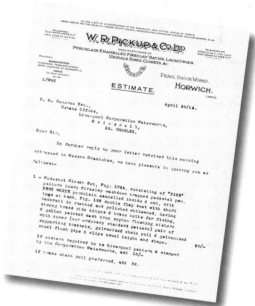

A W.R. Pickup & Co. Ltd. estimate for the supply of sanitary products to Liverpool Corporation's Waterworks at Brinscall, Near Chorley dated 30 April 1914.
Photo: Horwich Heritage Centre Collection

Two wonderfully evocative images depicting Fred in happy-go-lucky, ever-cheerful poses
Gordon Connolly Collection

A distinctive and important item of plant was the large coal-fired rotary kiln that Pickups operated for the firing of the fireclay products. The square 110 foot brick chimney, built in 1879, had been used until it became obsolete in the mid 1970s to provide draught for the refractory brick-making furnaces, the rotary kiln and the boilerhouse.

Fred's Chimney Drop

This was one of Fred's earliest televised chimney demolition jobs. The chimney was located close to several long brick-drying sheds with asbestos roofs. The sheds situated to the right of the stack were evidently of particular concern to Fred, for he was fully aware that when the chimney collapsed, it would strike the hard concrete surface of the Works Yard with significant force and should the mass of bricks fan out and strike the shed wall, it could cause them to collapse which would bring down the roofs. Pretty worrying scenario!

Fred and his much respected mate 'Owd Donald' had been hard at work for the previous four days, cutting the required 'gob' through five or six courses of hard brickwork and inserting the timber 'pit-props' to support the 110 feet of chimney towering above. On Thursday morning at 11 o'clock Fred, 'Owd Donald' and several of Pickup's hands commenced with the construction

of the bonfire. There was plenty of fire-raising material available comprising scores of massive tractor and lorry tyres, a couple of tons of old wooden planks, scrap timber pallets, and a large roll of bitumenised roofing felt, that oozed liquid pitch.

On him seeing the highly flammable roofing material, Fred excitedly shouted above the roar from a huge diesel-powered tractor, "It'll make some bloody black smoke, they'll think the Works are burning down".

Whilst all this bonfire building activity was taking place a large crowd had started to gather, many being school children from St. Catherine's School located close by, who had been given the morning off and formed a significant throng within the crowd. At 12 noon precisely Fred's wife Alison wearing a brightly checked tweed jacket and jeans lit the chimney's funeral pyre in time honoured fashion and the flames quickly spread throughout the large stack of diesel-soaked timber and huge tyres. Just as Fred had earlier prophesied, when the tarred roofing felt caught fire, the whole mass of rapidly burning material generated enormous clouds of black smoke that filled the skies above the Fireclay Works Yard.

Over ten years following the Pickup's Fireclay Works job, Fred related to me some of the concerns that he had endured whilst actually carrying out this particular chimney felling operation at Horwich.

Fred's Story:

"Because Pickup's chimney was situated close to several long drying sheds with asbestos roofs I were especially worried because when the chimney actually collapsed it would strike the yard surface, which were of concrete, with great force and should the mass of bricks fan out too far, then they could severely damage the shed walls, or worse still, knock them inwards which could bring down the roofs. Pretty worrying stuff, like, really. The other thing is that square chimneys can be reet awkward. If you were to leave, say, just a half brick on the right hand side, and you'd engineered it to fall slightly to the left hand side, then the damn thing would either decide to stay up, which is not only bloody embarrassing but dangerous too, or would fall more towards the right hand side where there might be a building or some other structure not needing the big hammer treatment. Also deadly and very costly! There's nearly always some clever sod in the crowd, one of them types who've just come along to witness a disaster, hoping you're gonna drop a clanger, who would suggest that I have'nt cut enough bricks out. But sometimes on certain chimneys it ain't as simple as that, for some bricks are extremely hard to chop through, whilst others can be dangerously soft and crumbly. It's these sort of things that you've got to take an account of. The main worry is even when you actually manage to get the stack to fall over, is the bloody thing gonna end up in the reet shop without smashing owt, or worse still, without any loose bricks landing on some poor sod's head? What has to be appreciated is that when you have a big chimney and you've lit the bumfire, its really thereafter out of your control so to speak. There's within the next ten to thirty minutes quite a large amount of nervous tension that builds up, but there's no way I want to show this anxiety to anyone, because if you were to go about as though you'd lost the plot, then everybody would think you were a sodding twit."

With the final collapse of the supporting pit-props the chimney commences to fall.
Gordon Connolly Collection

The massive bulk of Pickup's square brick 110 feet chimney breaks its back as it plummets to the ground exactly as calculated and engineered by Fred.
Gordon Connolley Collection

"With the Pickup's chimney, down it came and apart from a few odd bricks landing safely in the empty school yard, everything went just as we had planned. I got a telling off from some local council official who complained about the great clouds of thick black smoke that came from burning the huge stack of tyres. But like I told him, we needed the high temperature from the burning tyres which brought down the chimney right on cue, and safely. Although, thinking back, that smoke, Alan, bloody hell, it were worse than smoking several boxes of Capstan full strength cigs. It made you cough like crazy. Yeah, I were reet pleased with the Fireclay Work's chimney demo job. I felt very satisfied, I'd every confidence in that one, as we'd planned its downfall just right".

A triumphant Fred with cigarette in hand cheerfully poses for the camera amidst the debris of W.R. Pickup's Fireclay Works chimney.
Paul Donoghue Collection

SIZE HOUSE MILL CHIMNEY DROP, HASLINGDEN, ROSSENDALE, LANCASHIRE

Tuesday 12th January 1982

With snow on the ground, on Tuesday 12th January 1982, Size House Mill's chimney collapses to fall parallel to the historic mill buildings exactly as Fred had planned.
Photo: Helmshore Local History Society

SIZE HOUSE MILL, HASLINGDEN, ROSSENDALE

On the perishing cold morning of Tuesday the 12th of January 1982 Fred Dibnah and Donald Payton commenced with the construction of the Size House Mill chimney's funeral pyre. Because of the hard frost of the previous night, the surface of the old cobble stone mill yard was extremely slippery due to the covering of ice, and on the mill walls there was a liberal dusting of hoar frost that glistened in the weak winter sunlight.

Fred and Donald had previously commenced with the demolition of the circular 100 feet tall stone chimney which was discovered to be in a seriously corroded state, a few days earlier, when they had laddered and scaffolded it. At two o'clock in the afternoon Fred would light the demolition bonfire and shortly after the Size House Mill chimney would fall to the ground.

Size House Mill was situated on Manchester Road, Haslingden and was established circa 1780 as a textile mill. There is record of an inscribed stone tablet bearing the initials of the original owners of the mill: H. and E.O., and a date of 1842 which was set into a gable end. These initials belonged to Henry Ormerod and his wife Ellen who evidently took ownership of the mill between 1830 and 1840. Their two sons, John Ormerod and Thomas Livesey Ormerod founded the firm: T.L. Ormerod Brothers in 1858 and operated from another local mill called Snig Hole at Helmshore. Some time later, riding on the back of success, the firm expanded to larger premises at Clough End Mill in the hamlet of Hud Hey where they operated 710 looms weaving shirting and other cloths. By 1879, John and Thomas Livesey Ormerod had another 424 looms operating at Albion Mill in Helmshore. It was during this period that Size House Mill was used for sizing the hundreds of warps that were fed into the Ormerod's looms all over the district. Later, Size House Mill would become renowned for sizing warps for textile mills from all over Lancashire. In the early years of the twentieth century, both the Ormerod brothers died and the firm was taken over by the manager, Aaron Holt, who together with his brothers, converted the firm into a limited liability company which continued to operate at the mill.

The final nail in the coffin for this historic Rossendale textile firm which led to its closure, occurred when the mill's only Lancashire steam boiler, built in 1883 by Daniel Adamson of Dukinfield was condemned by the boiler inspector and the cost of a replacement boiler was quoted as £30,000. Apparently, mill owners and their engineers used to visit the mill just to see this venerable Lancashire boiler. Sadly, however, Size House Mill closed in 1978. By 1982, the historic, old mill buildings were empty and suffering the affects of the weather and from vandalism. Around this period Size House Mill was acquired by a firm of property developers who commenced with the demolition and clearance of the whole site to make way for a new residential development known as Size House Village.

Fred found the Size House Mill chimney demolition job quite a challenge due to the freezing weather conditions and later related the job to me in his usual enthusiastic style:

Fred's Story:

"The stone blocks that this chimney were built from were so badly corroded and rotten that you could crush them to dust with just a few taps with your hammer. In fact the carcase of the whole chimney was so poor, that when we laddered it, the dogs securing the two topmost ladders, when driven in, were held up by just a wing and a prayer. You see, Alan, we had decided to access the top forty foot so we could reduce the chimney in height down to about sixty foot which also reduced the weight of the stack considerably. This was because under t'mill yard there were a network of large sewer pipes that might have been severely damaged if I were to bring the whole chimney down on top of them. Anyway, once we had got the ladders up and the staging around the top, which were quite a bit dangerous like, due to the rotten stonework, knocking off the courses of stone were reet easy and we soon had the top off. After this work was finished me and Owd Donald got stuck in with relish into chopping out a wide 'gob' into the chimney base and fitting in the 'pit-props'. The stone at the base was in such a poor state that we could knock out most of the courses with just the hand hammer. We hardly used the air-hammer at all. It were, despite the freezing cold weather, easy work, not a bad job. On the Tuesday afternoon at 2 o'clock, with quite a large audience watching, I lit the bumfire which we'd piled up under the 'gob'. I stayed reet close to the rear end of the chimney watching out for movement. Whilst I did so, I were sipping a pint pot of hot tea laced with whisky provided by one of the development firm's managers and, by Hell's Teeth, I sure needed it, for it were freezing cold, even though I were only a couple of yards away from the heat of the bumfire. I kept taking a peek at the 'pit-props' which, after about twenty minutes were really

feeling the pain. At around 2.20 p.m. with plenty of black smoke belching out from the top of the chimney, I saw the badly charred timber props suddenly collapse and then the whole stack toppled in a sort of slow motion and then fell to hit the deck with an almighty crash. It was all over. I felt reet chuffed for it had toppled over and landed just as we had engineered it. Really, this small chimney were quite old, the stone blocks were rubbish but it were a good un, an easy un to drop."

These three Ransome's built Lancashire boilers set into an unidentified cotton mill boiler house would look similar to the 1883 Daniel Adamson Lancashire boiler that Size House Mill depended upon for steaming the mill's engine until it was sadly condemned by the Boiler Inspector.
©Alan McEwen Industrial Heritage Collection

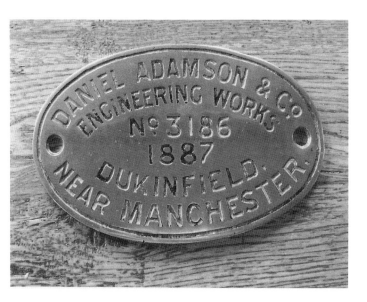

A brass makers plate from a Daniel Adamson Lancashire boiler No. 3186 of 1887.
©Alan McEwen Industrial Heritage Collection

The felling of Size House Mill Chimney.
This illustration is taken from a water colour painting by courtesy of
Robin Sharples of Cowpe, in Rossendale.

LABURNUM MILL CHIMNEY DROP, ATHERTON, NR. BOLTON

Sunday 13th November 1983

Laburnum Mill, Atherton circa 1980. This dramatic photograph depicts the massive mill block, the graceful 200 foot tall mill chimney with its attendant Engine and Boiler Houses and to the right of the picture the highly decorative Mill Tower with its date stone of 1905.
Copyright: Wigan Archives Service WLCT

The Laburnum Mill chimney job was always one of the more memorable of Fred's chimney drops, due to the downright bloody-minded antics of some young vandals who, whilst trespassing on the mill site, and discovering that the chimney's imminent demolition had been prepared by propping the gobbed mouth with pit-props in the base, actually set it on fire which resulted in the chimney dramatically collapsing very prematurely, and almost on top of Fred!

On numerous occasions during the following years, whether it be in a pub, on the site of another chimney drop, or even in Fred's Engine shed, Fred would often tell the dramatic story of what he termed, "THE LABURNUM MILL SAGA".

September 1982 and Fred with arms folded and a confident grin on his face poses for the camera in front of the 200 foot Laburnum Mill Chimney which he has laddered and scaffolded for a Granada Television production starring Timothy West and called 'Brass'. To the left above Fred's head are two of his famous 'flying buckets', used for lowering brickwork to the ground.
©Alan McEwen Industrial Heritage Collection

Fred's Story:

"Laburnum Mill were originally built around 1905. It must have been, because the massive mill engine that had powered all of the spinning frames and other machinery had been built in 1905 by Bolton steam engine makers, John and Edward Wood. On the few occasions that I actually worked carrying out chimney repairs like re-pointing and fettling the lightning conductor at Laburnum Mill, I would take the opportunity of seeing the ginormous engine which were a four cylinder, triple expansion type, steamed by four or five great Lancashire boilers operating at 180 pounds per square inch pressure. The engines were awesome in the power they produced, which were around 1800 horse power. They were beautifully painted, had tons of highly polished brasswork and were named 'Capital' and 'Labour'. Real beauties. This bonny mill engine

were smashed up in a bout of bloody legalized vandalism, sometime during the late 1960s when the mill's machinery became electrified. A hell of a pity!. The Laburnum Mill buildings which included an 170 feet tall decorative tower with loads of terracotta moldings and a 1905 date stone, a massive multi-storeyed spinning block, engine house and boilerhouse were very grand. The mill chimney was over 200 foot in height, built of brick and circular in shape. It had quite a large ornamental oversiller just under the cap stones; the whole chimney was mounted on a lovely ornate, square base. It was a truly beautiful chimney but was no longer needed once the mill closed in 1982. I were contracted to demolish this here chimney and the fancy terracotta mill tower as well".

"FELL WITH FRED"

Sunday 13th. November – 12.30pm

Laburnham Mill Chimney, Atherton.

Help Fred Dibnah fell this famous land mark.

Tickets – **25p**

In aid of the Cathy Hill Laser Fund

Hand Bill advertising Fred Dibnah's Laburnum
Mill chimney drop.
©*Alan McEwen Industrial Heritage Collection*

ATHERTON & TYLDESLEY ROUND TABLE
for cathy hill cancer research fund
welcome you to watch

laburnum chimmney
being
DEMOLISHED
by
FRED DIBNAH
on
SUNDAY NOV 13th at 12.30pm

No 002591
FRED DIBNAH
'FELL WITH FRED'
Name & Address:

FRED DIBNAH PRESENTS: No 002591

FELL WITH FRED

Draw to be held on 9th November 1983 at
Bolton Chronicle Office, Corporation Street, Bolton.

PRIZE

A chance to help Fred Dibnah to Fell the
200ft Chimney Stack at Laburnum Mill, Atherton
on Sunday 13th November 1983 at 11-00 a.m.
IN AID OF: CATHY HILL CANCER RESEARCH FUND
and Church of England Childrens Society.

Demolition Contractors: Walter Forshaws Ltd, Westhoughton.
Promoter: Ray Royle, 17 Greenfield Road, Atherton.
Registered with Wigan Metro.   TICKETS 25p EACH

Counterfoils and Monies
to be returned by
7th November 1983.

Raffle Ticket
©*Alan McEwen Industrial Heritage Collection*

"Just before we commenced the demolition preparations for the chimney, my wife Alison came up with a plan to generate money by running a sort of raffle in aid of cancer research. Her idea was that the person holding the winning ticket which were drawn on the morning of the actual chimney drop would assist me in lighting the demolition bumfire. This lighting of the bumfire job is summat that loads of people always seem to want to do. Most folk nowadays have hum-drum, boring jobs and lives, so to light the funeral pyre of a 200 foot mill chimney must obviously appeal to them. It's probably summat to do with an inner destructive urge that some folk are born with. Any road, the raffle went extremely well and we made over a thousand quid for the cancer charity.

Late on the Saturday evening before the Sunday morning of the planned chimney drop, I were reet tired as I'd been grafting on the preparations for its demise all that day, so I were just in the throes of going to bed when the bloody infernal telephone roared into life making me jump like hell. There were a lass on t'other end, who told me that some lads had set the pit-props alight and it were burning like the fires of Hell. 'Cos I were dead beat, I thought it were some kind of a prank. It turned out to be a police telephone operator and she were ringing me from a cop

shop over in Atherton. Then a copper came on the phone line and told me the chimney's supporting sticks had been on fire for almost an hour. I asked this copper if the chimney were still stood up. He said it were and that the fire brigade were at Laburnum Mill trying to put out the fire. Despite me being dog-tired, I told the copper that I'd make my way over to sort of recce the damage. I jumped int' Lanny and raced over to Atherton at break-neck speed.

On my arrival on the mill site it were pitch black, and I couldn't see either the Police or Fire Brigade who were supposed to be on site. I had difficulty walking over to the chimney base due to me tripping over all sorts of bloody junk. When I got there, I could just about see in the murk that the fire were out and an awful smell of burnt rubber filled the air. I then walked back to the Lanny for my torch which I had left in the cab. Making my way back to the chimney and glancing over towards the street I noticed a large fire engine parked in the road outside with a number of firemen stood alongside. I walked over and I asked the fire chief character in command if they'd put out the fire. The fire officer told me they had extinguished the fire but he wasn't going to order his firemen anywhere near the chimney again due to there being a large propane gas bottle stood right in the heart of the charred pit-

props. I couldn't believe what I were hearing and told them simply that because the propane bottle hadn't actually exploded during the hour it had stood in the fire, then there were no bloody way it were going to explode now. I then walked back to the area of the chimney base and with my torch I could see that all that remained of the 25 pit-props that we had fitted to support the chimney, there were now only three and they were severely fire ravaged. I found the propane gas bottle too, which were stood upright in the gob, the top valve had melted off and the bottle was totally empty.

What had obviously occurred were that these bloody mindless nutters had jammed the propane gas bottle in the midst of the timber pit-props, opened up the valve allowing the gas to escape, then lit it. This stupid act by these daft buggers made me realise how foolish it were to leave combustible materials anywhere near a gobbed out, pit-propped chimney base and to definitely never build a bumfire prior to the morning of the actual chimney drop, so I resolved that in future we wouldn't ever allow anyone to leave anything burnable near to any of our chimneys. In this case though, there hadn't been any scrap wood or tyres anywhere near the stack. I had made a point of telling the demolition men to keep all wood and tyres well away. Although I remember a roll of rubber roofing sheeting lying nearby. This is what must have caused the horrible rubbery stink, as the nutters must have pushed the rubber sheeting amongst the props to make them burn faster.

The good thing in all this, I considered, were that the chimney were still standing. But only just! I walked around to the opposite side of the gob to take a look at the horizontal crack that ran across the brickwork. To my horror, in the light of my torch I could see that there were no way I could attempt to re-prop the chimney, for it were totally unstable. This crack were now around 3/16th of an inch wide. But when we had left it late on Saturday afternoon it were then only 1/64th of an inch wide and extending to around eight feet of the chimney's girth. The bloody crack were now

almost fifty per cent around the circumference, which meant that due to the 200 feet height of the stack, at the top it would be about eighteen inches out of plumb and therefore ready for toppling. There were nowt either me or anyone else could do including the 'Man in the Sky'. Within a few minutes more you could hear the thing creaking and groaning and bits of brick and mortar were raining down. I decided it were high time to bugger off.

During the few minutes I had been inspecting the condition of the chimney a handful of firemen and several coppers had bravely advanced along the mill yard and were now standing just about 10 yards away from the chimney base and were setting up some powerful lighting equipment. I quickly joined them, and advised them to bugger off where it were safer down the road. We had only just cautiously walked about a hundred yards away in the opposite direction to the chimney's drop zone, when suddenly with a loud report that echoed all over the dark mill yard, the massive bulk of the Laburnum Mill chimney crashed down in a monster cloud of dust and flying brick rubble. The time was 1.45 a.m. on the Sunday morning. By heck, we were reet lucky.

It were all over for the beautiful Laburnum Mill chimney and extremely sad really because our non-event caused a major traffic jam during the following morning, due to interested people arriving who had travelled from all over the North to witness the chimney drop. But they were obviously severely disappointed. It taught me a lot did that one."

Fred subsequently carried out the demolition of the 170 foot decorative Mill Tower, which also gave him several headaches; but that's another story – see Laburnum Mill Tower Drop.

(Also see the Cockermouth Mill Chimney Drop where Fred was again troubled by vandals who set fire to the pit-props which resulted in a near tragedy).

LABURNUM MILLTOWER DROP, ATHERTON, NR. BOLTON

Sunday 8th January 1984

The Laburnum Mill Tower. Note the tablet with the inscribed date 1905, the ornate balcony with its ballustrading and the highly distinctive octagonal cupola and domed roof. A beautiful Edwardian structure.
Copyright: Wigan Archives Service WLCT

Notwithstanding the near tragedy of the early hours of Sunday 13th November 1983, when the Laburnum Mill chimney dramatically toppled which was the result of mindless arsonists firing the pit-prop supports, which almost buried Fred together with several police and firemen under a mountain of brick rubble, and moreover, despite some of the locals calling the mill site 'jinxed', two months later, Fred bravely tackled the awkward and dangerous demolition of the decorative Laburnum Mill Tower.

The 170 foot mill Tower which was highly ornamented with decorative terracotta moldings and a 1905 date stone took Fred several days of really hard graft to cut through the external walls on three sides, and also the more difficult work associated with the profoundly dangerous task of cutting out the internal stairwell support walls and fitting scores of pit-props all around. Fred related this particularly troublesome demolition job accompanied with much cursing on the same occasion he dramatically told me the story about the Laburnum Mill chimney collapse.

The massive gobbed-out and pit-propped frontage of the Mill Tower just prior to the demolition bonfire being constructed.
Harry Forshaw Collection

Fred's Story:

"I didn't really fancy carrying out the felling of the Laburnum Mill Tower, because everybody were telling me it were bloody jinxed. Normally I don't believe in all that hocus-pocus tripe, but I must admit the Laburnum Mill site and particularly that tall, gloomy Tower made me feel reet queer. There were summat odd about it. I even asked an old guy who had worked in't mill as a mechanic, if owt horrible had ever happened. But he said nowt had. But I kept thinking back to the early Sunday morning of the 13th November, when due to some idiots sticking a propane gas bottle amongst the supporting pit-props and setting it alight, the bloody 200 foot chimney, when it collapsed almost caused my demise.

On the upside, this would be my first Mill Tower demolition job – pretty exciting stuff, so I just got stuck in. When we were chopping out the brickwork to form a long gob in the Tower's outside walls, despite the bricks being reet hard like – I think they were Accrington NORI's, the job progressed really well, and I felt okay. But when we started to work on the base walls of the staircase right inside the Tower, I didn't like it. There were a queer sort of atmosphere, a bit

creepy like. It were really bloody dangerous too, and the bricks were even harder than the outside 'uns. So the chopping out and the pit-propping went on day after day and so we motored along until the job were fettled. There were still a sort of doom-laden feeling about the whole place, but I just sort of put it out of me mind.

On the Sunday morning of the drop we arrived on the Laburnum Mill site pretty early and after a brew and a fag or two, me and a few lads gathered massive piles of old wood and hundreds of tyres which we stacked all around the pit-props both inside and outside the Tower. Loads and loads of folk turned up to see this bloody great Mill Tower hit the deck. I'd asked the wife Alison to light the bumfire which she did at 12 o'clock. Then I lit the stairwell bumfire which I didn't like doing. Within say about ten minutes from Alison lighting the bumfire, it were blazing brightly like the fires of Hades. Tons of thick, black choking smoke poured out from not only the gob, but also from all of the window openings up the sides of the Tower which blackened the sky. The stink of the burning rubber tyres were horrible and the fumes made you shed buckets of tears. We must have blackened the whole of Atherton with rubber tyre smog."

Fred prepares the bonfire ignition torches for his wife Alison.
Harry Forshaw Collection

Fred inside the Mill Tower carrying out the exceedingly dangerous job of lighting the bonfire under the internal staircase.
Harry Forshaw Collection

A massive pall of pitch black smoke rises from the huge blazing bonfire to blacken out the sky.
Harry Forshaw Collection

"Whilst the fire was ravaging my pit-props I felt pretty nervous like, but I didn't show it to anyone. I kept pacing around the base of the Tower inspecting the pit-props which were all burning furiously and becoming thinner by the minute. After about twenty minutes, I heard a loud ripping sound pretty close to where I stood, then 'badoom', a mass of bricks started to rain down from one wall of the Tower as the pit-props ravaged by the bumfire suddenly keeled over. Then as fast as the fall of bricks had started, it just suddenly stopped. I made a quick inspection all around the base of the Tower, which revealed that most of the fire had died down and the majority of the supporting pit-props were no more. They'd all burnt away from the front and sides of

the gob. I could just make out through the large amount of smoke pouring from within the insides of the Tower that, despite the majority of the sticks being burned away that had been supporting the internal staircase, the whole Tower was still bloody upright. I could sense that the large crowd were thinking that I'd dropped a bollock which were a bit embarrassing like. I were confident that we had engineered the demolition totally correct. But here we were with a 170 foot Mill Tower with a large chunk of one wall fallen away, the bloody bumfire over and done with, and the Tower still standing. At this moment, even I thought the bloody Laburnum Mill site were jinxed! But I knew, I couldn't just leave it standing there for it were by now, extremely *dangerous. It were down to me to sort the job out, and rightly so.*

I got the mobile compressor fired up and holding onto my air-hammer and silently trusting that the Man in the Sky would look after me, I commenced to break out more bricks along both sides of the external gob. A pretty dangerous job! Whilst I were chiselling, I were keeping an eye out for cracks that I knew must start running shortly, for there were nowt holding the Tower up, but perhaps the internal staircase brickwork. So I kept chopping out first one wall, then moving around to the opposite one. All of a sudden, I could see bloody great ginormous horizontal cracks starting to race all across the brickwork. So I buggered off out of the way as fast as quicksilver dragging me trusty air-hammer and air pipelines with me."

Right: Huge orange flames hungrily devour the pit-props supporting the Tower.
Harry Forshaw Collection

A large amount of brickwork dramatically falls from the Tower (left) …………. and despite most of the props having been burnt away……… (right) the Tower remains stubbornly standing with steam issuing from the bottom.
Harry Forshaw Collection

"Glancing over my shoulder, I saw massive chunks of brickwork suddenly commence falling from the damaged side of the Tower, then the whole structure rapidly disintegrated and collapsed in a gigantic heap wreathed in black smoke and massive clouds of dust. The Laburnum Mill Tower, were done for. It were no more! What a bloody, deadly doom-laden job! I were reet glad to see all that fancy terracotta and brickwork sat on the deck. Following a few pints, I felt the gloom sort of lift away. What a bloody weird job we did at Laburnum Mill."

Fred went on to tell me he reckoned that he hadn't cut enough brickwork out of the internal staircase gob and the pit-props were far too short. A most dangerous learning curve. He did say, however, that despite the gloomy sensation, there were several moments of immense excitement which thrilled him and made the job worthwhile.

When Fred demolished the Dart Mill Tower in Bolton in 1985, he made adjustments regarding the height of the pit-props, based on his experience at Laburnum Mill.

Right: Finally following Fred's brave exploits involving the profoundly dangerous job of chiselling out extra brick work, the Laburnum Mill Tower disintegrates with bricks flying all over the place as the structure dramatically collapses to the ground.
Harry Forshaw Collection

Yellow helmeted firemen stare into the huge pile of rubble, all that remains of the once proud Laburnum Mill Tower whilst scores of excited onlookers move forward.
Harry Forshaw Collection

STANHILL RING SPINNING MILL CHIMNEY DROP, WEST END, OSWALDTWISTLE, LANCASHIRE

Friday 18th January 1985

Winter 1983 and the once-proud Stanhill Ring Mill forlornly stands vandalised awaiting its ultimate fate: demolition. The tall red brick chimney awaits its demise too.
Mike Rothwell Collection

This memorable chimney demolition job at Stanhill Ring Spinning Mill involved, not only Fred, but also a dare-devil, expert stuntsman racing car driver, Dutchman, Dickie Beer. During the passage of Fred's long steeplejacking career, he has been featured in all types of promotional films and television commercials ranging from breakfast cereals which was actually filmed in South Africa through roofing slate manufacture to extolling the virtues of quaffing a Lancashire brewery's best bitter.

Stanhill Ring Mill's once attractive Engine House now with sightless windows and the base of the 140 foot cylindrical chimney photographed in the winter of 1983.
Mike Rothwell Collection

A household name motor car sales group, on hearing that Fred Dibnah, the nationally-renowned steeplejack, chimney felling expert and television personality was going to demolish one of Oswaldtwistle's finest mill chimneys: a much-loved local landmark, decided to use the event to promote one of their upmarket and expensive cars, the V.W. Scirocco. A London-based advertising agency brought over from Holland the expert stunt-driver, Dickie Beer to prove that the new Volkswagen Scirocco could accelerate at great speed away from underneath Fred's toppling 140 foot mill chimney. Fred was asked if he would work with Dickie, and enthusiastically agreed that he would be delighted to do so.

On the early morning of Friday the 18th of January 1985 in atrocious wintry conditions of falling snow and severe frost, Dutch stuntman driver Dickie Beer commences with a test run of the VW Scirocco car by sprinting it down a specially prepared tarmac road away from the chimney which has been previously prepared for demolition by Fred.
Paul Donoghue Collection

During the previous week prior to the chimney drop, whilst Fred and his mate Donald were busily engaged in gobbing out and propping up the base of the chimney, which was carried out in atrocious conditions of heavy snow falls and freezing cold, a large number of the film company's personnel were also hard at work at the Stanhill Ring Mill site, making preparations for the forthcoming dramatic event which included the laying down of a tarmacadam road running out from the chimney base to a far extremity of the mill yard.

The large splendidly designed red brick Stanhill Ring Spinning Mill prominently stood out amongst the surrounding stone-built terraced houses and weaving sheds so typical of East Lancashire mill towns and was a highly regarded, local landmark. The mill had been erected in 1907 by the Stanhill Ring Spinning Company Limited, the architecturally merited design by mill architects Fox, Son & Hemmings of Manchester; the actual builders were R. Shorrock & Sons of Darwen. Within the distinctive engine house a Yates & Thom horizontal compound mill engine rated at 1850 I.H.P. which had a massive flywheel grooved for 48 cotton ropes provided the power to operate the mill's 72,000 ring spindles, supplied and installed by Howard and Bullough Ltd of Accrington. Within the four storeyed manufactory there were originally 500 operatives employed spinning American yarns.

Following the end of the First World War the mill's directors reconstituted the business which was then called The Stanhill Ring Spinning Company (1920) Limited. During the 1930s the number of ring spinning spindles had increased to a total of 87,000. In 1955, English Sewing Cotton purchased the company and would later re-equip the mill with more modern spinning machinery. However, during the years following, increasing foreign imports of cotton goods, forced the profitability of the company in a downwards spiral which led to closure of the Stanhill Ring Spinning Company Ltd in June 1980.

In 1987, a last ditch attempt to resurrect the fortunes of the old mill commenced when cotton spinning entrepreneur, Colin Nelson of Great Harwood, near Blackburn, formed the Stanhill Spinning Company and re-opened the mill for business.

Sadly, despite considerable effort and enterprise, the new venture only lasted a year and closed down finally in 1982. The fine mill buildings thereafter stood idle and became partially vandalised until the whole, once proud mill complex was demolished 1984-1985. The streets of terraced houses in West End, were locally known as 'Little Wigan', due to large numbers of early cotton operatives originating from the Wigan area.

Due to the Stanhill Ring Spinning Mill chimney drop being carried out by Fred during a mid-week period, regrettably I didn't attend this most spectacular event. I did however, view the drama of that cold January morning at Stanhill when later I saw the V.W. Scirocco commercial on the television. Around a fortnight later, upon visiting Fred in his workshop, he greatly entertained me by relating to me, 'The Stanhill Ring Mill Chimney Felling Job'.

Fred's Story:

"Me and Donald had prepared the 140 foot brick chimney over the previous few days in absolutely perishing cold weather. Some mornings due to snow and icy conditions we were quite late arriving up there in Oswaldtwistle, it were so bad. Anyway, this film outfit rang me up from London to ask me if I would take part in a television film they wanted to make to promote a car. The idea was for a stunt-driver in this here new Volkswagen car which was worth about ten grand, one hell of a lot o' brass, to drive away fast from the chimney base just as the chimney were about to fall. I told them, I would do it as it sounded reet exciting.

Anyway after working for three days cutting through the bricks which were of good quality and reet hard, we got the thing set up on the sticks and ready for the drop. On the morning of the chimney drop we arrived at Stanhill Mill at 8 o'clock and it were brass monkeys freezing cowd with freshly fallen snow covering the mill yard and still quite dark. There were scores of these here film-making types, all weirdly togged up in arctic-weather gear, all standing about with some very expensive-looking camera tackle. They had a mobile canteen, a sort of owd bus which was serving tasty bacon butties and tea. Me and Owd Donald were served some breakfast from this bus and it didn't cost us owt.

A bit later on I met Dickie Beer the stunt-driver and he were quite a cool lad. He told me he were looking forward to me dropping the chimney because this would be his first."

The final run: with the chimney's funeral pyre furiously blazing at the rear, Dickie commences to gun the VW forward at breakneck speed.
Paul Donoghue Collection

"This film agency lot really wanted to keep the chimney dropping event secret, but hundreds of folk turned up including lots of school kids despite the dreadful weather conditions. There were quite a few coppers and firemen and even an ambulance crew on hand, just in case I dropped the bloody Stanhill Mill chimney on top of the car.

At around 12.20 we lit the large bumfire that we'd stacked around the pit-props. It didn't take long, there were bloody great clouds of reet dense black smoke pouring out the chimney top. Some of the firemen didn't appreciate the loads of big bright orange sparks that were dropping onto the nearby house roofs as well. Dickie the Dutchman were sat in his beautiful brand new motorcar positioned, just as we'd planned, slightly to one side of the chimney's chopped out gob, waiting for me to give him the green light to bugger off fast, by the sounding of my bulb horn. It just looked like he were dead in line with the path of the chimney when it fell, but he actually weren't. His position had been carefully engineered and I had every confidence that he would be safe. All around the site, the film cameramen squinted through their television cameras looking reet nervous."

Dickie accelerates the VW Scirocco safely away from the toppling 140 foot chimney.
Newspaper Cutting: Courtesy of Lancashire Evening Telegraph 19th January 1985.

FRED DIBNAH'S CHIMNEY DROPS

"Within just over 10 minutes from lighting the bumfire, I saw that the pit-props were really feeling the pain, then suddenly they started to buckle causing the Stanhill Mill chimney to shudder. Dickie's small face peeping out from his tin crash hat were looking towards me. I could sense his pent up tension as he revved up the car's engine. I quickly sounded me bulb horn as the chimney commenced to topple over in slow motion and then fall. Out of the corner of me eye, I saw Dickie's Volkswagen car screaming along the new tarmac road at one hell of a rate of knots, and with a great thundering crash the Stanhill Mill chimney hit the deck. It did appear as if the stack were sort of chasing Dickie's car, but he were well out of the way. Everything happened so fast.

One or two of the cameramen told me afterwards that it appeared as if the whole plan had gone tragically wrong and the massive chimney looked as if it were falling right on top of Dickie's car and they had held their breath for the split second it took the stuntman to make his getaway. It were a near thing though, for a few flying bricks actually struck and damaged his brand new motor car."

Fred went on to inform me that Dickie Beer, whom I didn't know of, was a most famous stuntman who had carried out some very dangerous stunts in a number of the James Bond and Indiana Jones films. He finished his exciting tale by expressing tremendous respect for the dare-devil bravery of the Dutch stuntman.

Made it! The car is virtually unscathed as the giant chimney crashes to the ground.
Newspaper Cutting: Courtesy of Lancashire Evening Telegraph 19th January 1985.

Well done mate! Dickie gives a somewhat embarrassed Fred, a quick peck on the cheek. Fred probably said "Well you know what these 'ere Continentals are like!"
Paul Donoghue Collection

STANHILL RING SPINNING MILL, OSWALDTWISTLE

The well-known Lancastrian author and poet the late Mrs. Benita Moore A.L.A. of Rising Bridge, near Accrington penned this wonderful evocative poem in memory of the Stanhill Ring Mill Chimney:

O'er t' West End of Ossie
Fer 77 years
There's a Lancashire landmark
That's moved folk to tears.
Stretching up to the sky
Wi'its back to the hills
Is the soot-blackened chimney
Of Stanhill Ring Mill.

Decade after decade
In 6am fogs
The cobbled yard echoed
To the clatter of clogs.
To girls in sack aprons –
Wi shawls round ther heads
Or lads in cloth caps
Coming straight from ther beds.

Rosy-cheeked, dewy-eyed
Rubbint sleep from ther "een"
Yet allus particular
To keep thersells clean.
These young lads 'n lasses
Prepared to do graft
At spinning an muling
Alongside ther dads.

Stanhill Mill were resplendent
When it wer first built
Majestic an formal
Right up to the hilt.
Chimney wer a landmark
A proud monument –
A symbol of prosperous
Money well spent!

During 't 50's and 60's
The mill had a ball
And 't chimney were sentin
Over 'em all.
Order books were full
There wer plenty to do
An it wasn't just work
For the fortunate few.

But now times have changed
An wer back to depression
The dole queues grow longer
Wer in a recession.
The spinners an weavers
Are thrown on the dole
But the mill has the cruellest
Fate of them all.

Gone are the clogs
An the shawls an the caps
The old mill is silent –
There's no spinners' laughs.
Stanhill Mill's up for sale
An all Ossie's heartbroken –
Thow'd chimney's still there
But it's only a token.

Empty and desolate
The mill stands and waits
For some magic miracle
To settle its fate.
The workers stand glumly
Gazing through locked gates
But there's no work for them
I'm afraid it's too late.

The chimney stands guard
Over't West End of town
But not for much longer
It's due to come down.
Fred Dibnah's in charge
With his organisation
But when he gets ont' job
Ther'll be no celebrations.

So it's goodbye owd friend
Tha's done thy job well
An mony folks gather
To hear the death knell.
There's not a dry eye
As ther comes a loud rumble
Ant thowd Stanhill Mill chimney
Has ten its last tumble.

By kind permission of Mr. Gordon Moore

DART MILL TOWER DROP, UNION STREET, BOLTON.

Sunday 22nd September 1985

The partially demolished Dart Mill and its distinctive tall tower with its name DART picked out in white glazed brick.
Anthony Green Collection

Although untypical of Fred's usual chimney demolition jobs, the felling of the Dart Mill Tower by Fred's 'cut, pit-prop and burn' procedure was so unique and indeed exceedingly dramatic and which portrayed the Boltonian Master Steeplejack at his most inventiveness, confident and daring; in other words Fred Dibnah at his best, that I have opted to include this fascinating story, particularly in light of the problems he experienced at his first mill tower drop at Laburnum Mill:

My recollection of the Sunday morning of the 22nd September 1985, was that for once we were blessed with fine and sunny conditions. Excellent weather for the demolition of mill chimneys, or, as in this case, a massively built brick Mill Tower.

Fred had telephoned me around a fortnight prior to the day of the demolition and invited me to the event. As the 22nd of September moved nearer I could feel my excitement rising and I was therefore really looking forward to witnessing the felling of the Dart Mill Tower, particularly so, because as Fred had explained to me, the demolition of the Tower was considerably more technical to prepare and carry out, was considered to be an extremely dangerous venture as indeed was the first mill tower demolition job that he had tackled at Laburnum Mill, Atherton in January 1984.

About 8.30 a.m. on the Sunday morning, I was just about ready to leave Farling Top and to drive the thirty two miles over the Pennine hills to Bolton, when the telephone rang. It was my foreman Boilermaker Michael who reported that they were experiencing problems with a boiler which my firm was repairing in a mill in Darwen.

DART MILL TOWER, BOLTON

Michael and another two of my boilermakers had been carrying out the partial retubing of this large Economic boiler the previous day, which involved the renewing of several dozen of the smoke tubes. However, every time the hydraulic test was applied, several more of the remaining original smoketubes would commence leaking. The problem was that the owners of the mill required steam at 7.0 a.m. on Monday morning to enable the factory to work. I decided therefore, that I would drive to Bolton via Darwen, which would enable me to join Michael at the mill and tender him some alternative instructions regarding our retube job, even though my visit would cause me perhaps an hour's delay, I would still have sufficient time left to attend Fred's demolition spectacle in good time, the event being timed for 1 o'clock.

On my arrival in the Darwen mill's boilerhouse, and closely inspecting the severely leaking smoke tubes in the Economic boiler, resulted in me instructing my men to cut out and remove another twenty condemned tubes, which regrettably, forced my hand to join them and assist with the extra work involved. As I was the boss of the firm, I felt that I had no other option but to work with my men, who were all extremely tired and to complete the job. I also considered it was the right decision, in respect also for my valued clients who were desperate to have the boiler repairs completed and the boiler back into steam.

All that long Sunday morning I found myself incarcerated in the filthy, and dusty old Darwen cotton mill boilerhouse helplessly watching the minutes on my wrist-watch race by as my men and I grappled with the retubing work on the ancient, rust-stained and asbestos-clad Economic boiler that the cotton mill so depended on. Oh! The joys of boiler engineering, I pondered.

When I was eventually satisfied with our efforts which was approved by the Boiler Inspector who had been standing by, after quickly scrubbing the muck and grime from my face and hands and throwing off my sooty boilersuit, I jumped into my Trooper four-wheel drive car, and raced the ten miles over the busy Pennine trunk road, the A666 and down into Bolton. It was by now, late afternoon and when I drove into Union Street, all that greeted me was a gigantic mountainous heap of still-smouldering brick rubble: all that remained of the Dart Mill Tower. For I had sadly missed the spectacular demolition job by three hours, and by this time, Fred, his task completed had departed the Dart Mill site to celebrate his success in a local public house.

The Dart Mill was originally designed by the renowned Oldham architect, P.S. Stott who had a reputation for designing distinctive and impressive mill buildings including some very fine, ornate Towers like for example, Arrow Mill, Castleton near Rochdale and Gorse Mill, Chadderton, near Oldham. Dart Mill was built in 1908 by the Dart Mill Spinning Co. (1906) Limited as a cotton-spinning mill.

Notwithstanding my profound disappointment at missing the Dart Mill Tower drop, during the following Tuesday evening, I found myself sat around the warm pot-bellied cast iron stove in Fred's 'hen-hut' workshop, listening in awe as Fred related 'the saga of the Dart Mill Tower demolition' in the most amazing and lucid detail, as we supped from bottles of the 'black nectar', as he called his favourite tipple – Guinness

Dart Mill Tower constructed from Accrington brick and terracotta mouldings with the name of the mill DART proudly displayed in white glazed brick.
Anthony Green Collection

FRED DIBNAH'S CHIMNEY DROPS

Fred's Story:

"I'd only knocked down one mill tower before I tackled Dart Mill Tower and that one didn't really go to plan. What it did do though were teach me a lot about the necessary preparation for the demolition of such tall, meaty structures. When I quoted Harry (the demolition contractor) my price of eight hundred quid it sort of started a friendly bidding war between us. Harry reckoned his men could drop the Tower using a big crane and swinging iron ball for six hundred quid. Anyway after a fair bit of bartering I had to drop me price and we shook hands on me doing the job for six hundred and fifty pounds.

Before I actually started the project, I got Harry to instruct his crane driver to belt off some of the large lumps of ragged brickwork still hanging from the part of the structure that had originally been built into the mill building, and they did it right away. On the morning that me and my mate Ronnie commenced chiselling out the brickwork at the base of the Tower, which was on raised ground and therefore gave me a panoramic view of this forgotten area of Bolton, which made me feel quite sad really, because the mills were standing empty and many were vandalised, I were dropping more and more chimneys, and it gave me a sort of empty feeling, because I knew at this rate, there'd be nowt left standing in Bolton, but the Town Hall clock tower.

With the Dart Mill Tower job Al, there were a reet lot of chopping out of the brickwork to form the usual gob or mouth type of opening on the dropside, and particularly so inside the building, where we had to break out the brickwork all around the base of the internal staircase, a massively built and extremely heavy structure. The stairs themselves were made from huge stone slabs, and there were about seven flights. These stairs had served the floors in the adjoining seven storey mill, which had suffered the big hammer treatment and been totally demolished.

You've heard the tale of Joshua and the Wall's of Jericho," Fred inquired. I shook my head, myself not being religious in the slightest, or having read the bible.

"Yeah, Joshua's army was attacking the city of Jericho, but couldn't breach the city walls until he came up with his grand plan, which involved his men undermining the walls and then placing numbers of wooden props underneath for support. They then built a massive bumfire beneath which burnt the props, resulting in the city walls collapsing and Joshua's victorious army then charged through the gaps to plunder the city and kill everyone", explained Fred with great excitement.

"Anyway, me and Ronnie got stuck into the cutting out of the brickwork on the first morning, with everything going really well. But at around 11 o'clock the BBC television crew arrived and asked us to stop work until they got their cameras and sound gear set up. I knew the director guy, who appeared really excited and told me that they were going to make a film of the whole job, which would make bloody brilliant television. It was dinner time before they were ready to film. After our dinner, me and Ronnie recommenced chopping out the bricks which were quite soft really and the job progressed very well. For every foot we cut out we placed an 18 inch tall pit prop, a cap piece and then drove in two wooden wedges. The job took us a few days of chopping out and propping, the Tower's external wall on the dropside and the two bits we cut out of the two side walls were quite easy. The hard graft came when we commenced cutting out the internal staircase walls deep inside the Tower. It were obviously extremely dangerous work as well, for you knew that there were several hundred tons of masonry rising up above your head, and unlike when you are working on a chimney outside in the open air, where you can see everything and can bugger off – if anything nasty is going to occur, inside the mill Tower, it just felt like being incarcerated deep in the bowels of a coal pit. Bloody dangerous stuff, but it sure got the adrenalin flowing. In all, we inserted around thirty pit-props in the Tower's external gobbed-out section including the side bits, and around twenty to support the staircase.

On the morning of the drop, which were quite fine with the sun shining for once, we stacked a huge amount of scrap timber in amongst the pit-props. They were some wagon tyres, but not enough and this gave me some concerns as we would require the tremendous heat that only tyres will produce to burn and weaken the large quantity of pit-props. But I knew it would be alreet, providing we packed plenty of this here bumfire material, not only in the gob, but particularly around the pit-props supporting the stone staircase which had a phenomenal weight pressing down from the seven flights above.

At the allotted time, I got a young local lass to light the fire. As you know Al, I don't like starting the bumfire myself as I have certain superstitious feelings – like it might go wrong!"

Fred stoops over to pick up a bucket filled with diesel oil.
Stan Holt Collection

Fred at the base of the Tower hurls a bucket full of diesel onto the heaped up timber and lorry tyres forming the demolition bonfire which will encourage it to burn once lit.
Stan Holt Collection

"The wood was nice and dry and we encouraged it to fiercely burn by chucking loads of diesel oil all over it. After the tyres caught, huge plumes of black smoke poured out from all over the Tower which got into your throat and made your eyes water. The fire had been burning for only a few minutes when you could hear the sound of sirens getting louder and louder and then the fire brigade arrived. Some silly sod must have 'phoned 'em. There's some nutters about! Anyway they soon went away, the police on the site must have told them everything was under control.

I kept walking round and round the Tower, but due to the large amount of black smoke, scrambling over the rubble were quite dangerous. In fact I very nearly fell down the steep slope to the front of the gobbed-out section of the Tower. I then saw a massive crack opening up on one of the corners of the structure. Within a couple of minutes a gigantic lump fell off from the cracked area. By this time I could see that the pit-props supporting the gob were buckling under the enormous weight and I knew it wouldn't be long before summat happened."

Fred instructs Debbie, a young local girl to light the bonfire.
Stan Holt Collection

Fred pokes the fire to ensure it has taken hold.
Stan Holt Collection

"I still kept walking round the base of the Tower holding onto me klaxon horn, but the smoke made my observations very difficult. I sensed that by this time there would perhaps be a small handful of pit-props still giving support within the staircase inside the Tower. Looking up I could see what I thought were rivulets of silvery rain pouring down the sides of the Tower from high up on the roof. It were molten lead that were pouring down. Bloody deadly stuff!

All of a sudden, there was movement, and then the massive brick Tower started to quickly disintegrate with several hundred tons of brick, stone, castiron and roof slate thundering down earthwards. It were really dramatic. I were very close, yes dangerously close – so I ran away like hell. I then blew my klaxon horn. It were soon all over and I were extremely pleased that we had done our job well and I also felt relieved. Some chap came out of the crowd and asked if I ever worried. I told this guy that I always worry, and it'd take a bloody brave man to tackle a large building with a box o'matches and not worry."

A dramatic scene as the fire rages under the stricken Tower and black smoke fills the sky.
Paul Donoghue Collection

Destructive force: this image was made through the chain-link fence and depicts the Dart Mill Tower breaking up and crashing down to the ground.
Stan Holt Collection

PARK MILL CHIMNEY DROP, HOLLINWOOD, OLDHAM

February 1986

The morning of the chimney drop and 'Fred's bumfire' consisting of scrap timber, old wooden pallets and scores of tyres are expertly stacked in and around the gob at the base of the chimney. Television sound and camera men are busily recording the scene.
Paul Donoghue Collection

This extremely dramatic chimney drop which was filmed by the BBC and featured on the popular programme 'A YEAR WITH FRED' gave Fred quite a shock due to the chimney suddenly collapsing without warning.

Park Mill was a typical Oldham district mill building constructed in the vernacular style circa 1860 by Joseph Baxter & Sons who lived at nearby Park House, Hollinwood.

Between 1884 and 1889 Park Mill was operated by Joseph Bowker & Co. Ltd. The mill was extended in 1908 and updated machinery installed. By 1933, all cotton production had ceased. Park Mill was later used by Smith & Nephew Ltd for the manufacture of children's clothing, but by the mid 1980s had closed down. The mill was demolished late 1985 and early 1986.

During one of Fred's many visits to Farling Top, whilst ensconced on the Chesterfield sofa with a glass each of the finest Yorkshire ale, brewed down in nearby Keighley, we watched the video of the Park Mill chimney drop. Fred and I were discussing the finer points of chimney demolition procedures in between taking large gulps of the tasty ale and devouring a plate piled high with wedges of Airedale's best pork pie.

At the end of the film when the Park Mill chimney collapses without Fred's usual honking of his air-horn, Fred turned round to me and exclaimed, *"Alan, cock, that chimney were a reet bizarre bugger which almost dropped right down on top of us all. A strange 'un, but I must have been saved by the 'Man in the Sky'."*

One of the young lasses, Debbie receives instructions from Fred on how to light the chimney's funeral pyre, whilst an excited Fred clutches an improvised bonfire lighting torch made from an old mop. In the background is the Oldham Council's 'brew cabin'.
Paul Donoghue Collection

Fred's Story:

"Me mate Harry Forshaw of Forshaw's Demolition gave me the job of demolishing the Park Mill chimney which were about 150 feet high and quite graceful. A nice chimney with a very beautiful top.

Anyway when I turned up on the mill site to view the job, Harry who were already there appeared to be quite concerned that the chimney were very close to the gable end of the nearest couple of semi-detached houses. I paced out the distance which amounted to thirty six feet which were close, but it didn't bother me and I told Harry so. To prove my confidence, I offered to stand in this here thirty six foot gap whilst the chimney collapsed. Harry were also concerned about the

close proximity of an electric board substation, but because he knew me so well, and appreciated that I had never done any serious damage, gave me the green light, provided I could get the necessary insurance cover.

Like I said to Harry, most of these insurance men are as timid as rabbits. They just stick a compass in the map of the area where the chimney waiting to be demolished is sited, and anything within one and a half the height of the chimney for three hundred and sixty degrees is deemed dead in their eyes. It makes my blood boil. How do these buggers keep their posh jobs, with their offices wi' carpets a foot thick. They drive about in Mark Ten Jaguars too! Anyway, I got the insurance cover sorted out, but the price were a whopping three grand. Daylight robbery!

PARK MILL, HOLLINWOOD, OLDHAM

The day dawned and it were wet and quite windy when we commenced with chopping out the bricks at the base of the chimney. These bricks were rotten, very soft and crumbly like. Nevertheless, it didn't take long for me and my mate Trevor to chop out a wide gob and get the stack set up on a few rows of pit-props.

On the morning of the chimney drop we arrived on the mill site and everything was drenched through for it had been raining cats and dogs all night. I'd been a bit concerned about the bumfire wood getting pissed through, but we found it were alreet because one of the demolition lads had conveniently dropped a wagon sheet over the pile. Anyway, there were tons o' scrap car and wagon tyres available. By about 10.30 a.m., me, Trevor and several other lads had built this superb bumfire which we had packed solid with loads of tyres. It were going to make one terrible blaze.

At eleven o'clock, dead on the dot, I instructed two young lasses to light the fire, whilst I drenched the wood and tyres with gallons of diesel oil. Whoosh! In no time at all, the bumfire was burning like the flames of Hell. Within a few minutes, when I looked up at the top o' chimney, there were masses of dense black smoke billowing upwards turning the day into night. Hell, the stink from the burning tyres, it were like a mixture of the local abattoir, the sewage works and the gas works! It were horrible and it made us all cough and retch and my eyes watered. No wonder the men from the Town Hall moan like buggery about me using tyres on me bumfires.

The black stinking smoke made your mouth taste like rotting flesh from a coffin. I cadged some chewing gum from one of the lasses to chase away the bad taste. Me and Trevor were sort o' squatting at the rear of the gob looking out for the tell-tale cracks, but nowt seemed to be happening. After several minutes longer, I chanced a quick gander around the left hand side of the gob and noticed that most of the sticks were burnt away. Hell what's holding the bugger up? Then I sensed summat were going to happen and I shouted to Trevor to bugger off quick."

The bonfire has been lit and the flames spread rapidly through the heap of combustible material.
Paul Donoghue Collection

Without warning the tall chimney suddenly starts to dramatically corkscrew down to earth with a massive roar as the bonfire blazes furiously. Fred and Trevor just about manage to escape.
Paul Donoghue Collection

A close-up study of the rapidly disintegrating chimney.
Paul Donoghue Collection

A dramatic shot of Fred and Trevor racing for their lives as the chimney tumbles down to the ground.
Paul Donoghue Collection

"Both of us had just moved a few yards towards an Oldham Council mobile brew cabin, when there were a terrific ripping sound. Glancing over me shoulder to my horror, I saw the Park Mill chimney suddenly disintegrating and sort of cork-screwing itself down into a massive dusty, smoky heap. It were just a few yards away! How it missed us both, I'll never know. I then blew hard on a silver Police whistle that I'd borrowed earlier from one of the coppers. I were quite shaken. But I'm sure no-one could tell.

When I'd quickly regained my wits, I joked with the large crowd that had surged forward. I pointed to a stunted sycamore tree that were close to the steaming mountain of crushed brick and told them all that the little tree were saved because it had a preservation order on it."

After draining the ale from the bottom of his glass, Fred turned around to me and brightly exclaimed that the Park Mill Chimney Drop had been a good un. One of the best. It had got his adrenalin flowing. It had excited him.

Fred finished his tale by telling me that he'd had every ounce of confidence in that chimney, we then got stuck in afresh to more Yorkshire ale and Airedale pork pie.

HOOLE BANK BRICKWORKS CHIMNEY DROP, MICKLE TRAFFORD NEAR CHESTER

Tuesday 22nd December 1987

The Hoole Bank Brickwork's bonfire had been lit by Fred and the well-established raging fire has seriously weakened the supporting pit-props resulting in the acute angle of the stack seconds before it collapsed.
Ray Willoughby Collection

This is the story of Fred's nerve-racking, deadly life-threatening experience of the Hoole Bank Brickworks chimney demolition which was related to me in the comfort zone of my warm office by Fred himself whilst he was ensconced within the depths of a leather armchair, a tumbler of single malt whisky in his hand, following him getting drenched by falling into a local river.

With the malt's wonderful restorative powers clearly working, Fred commenced narrating the drama involved at the Hoole Bank Brickworks site, by cheerily stating that when he is ever near to water: canals, rivers, lakes etc., because he cannot swim, he is always particularly careful. But accidents can and do happen:..... so firstly let me explain how Fred had become wet through……

Back in the early 1990's Fred and Sue Dibnah and their two young sons, Jack and Roger, used to visit Farling Top Farm quite regularly where the boys would enjoy playing with my son Alasdair and daughter Shonagh. Fred was always keen to walk around the Boilerwork's yard and Workshops, where he would closely inspect and comment upon the boiler work being carried out on traction engines and railway locomotive boilers. He was particularly interested in flanging work on firebox end plates or riveting jobs.

Whilst Sue was being entertained in the farmhouse by my former wife Maria, Fred and I would take the golden opportunity to disappear for a couple of hours, usually to trolley around Keighley or Skipton, or over the Lancashire/Yorkshire border where we explored numerous old cotton and woollen mills and other historically noteworthy industrial sites. I particularly recall Fred's expression of amazement when I showed him the gigantic indoor waterwheel built around the 1860s at Dale End Mill, Lothersdale. Our visit resulted in Fred explaining in great detail his enthusiastic account of how - if time and money permitted - he would set about renovating and restoring the massive 45 feet diameter waterwheel built of cast and wrought iron and timber and to get it revolving once again. I was impressed with Fred's obvious deep understanding of the mechanical wizardry of the giant waterwheel with its many iron spidery spokes, its oily cogs, shafts and bearings - and even the hand-wrought iron nuts and bolts that held it together.

Prior to Fred's visit to Farling Top Farm, I would usually plan a whistle-stop tour of any local historically noteworthy sites, for I fully appreciated Fred's profound interest and boundless

enthusiasm for historic mechanical engineering sites and old industrial ruins. It was patently obvious to me, that my old friend Fred Dibnah thoroughly enjoyed these outings in Pennine West Yorkshire and the Pendle district of Lancashire, where the enigmatic and often beguiling historic industrial sites of old stone built cotton and woollen mills, lead mines, tall chimney stacks and a wealth of historic architectural delights abounded amongst the wild moorland and beautiful hill country.

Both Fred and I always got on like the proverbial house on fire, and both of us had a mutual respect for each other's professions and also enjoyed all aspects of steam and mechanical engineering; we were after all, formed from the very same mould: both fellow Lancastrians, both born in mill towns, Fred in Bolton, whilst I originated from the cotton town of Middleton, near Rochdale.

LOW BRIDGE MILL RIVER PLUNGE ADVENTURE, KEIGHLEY

It's a Jack Frost cold March morning in 1992. The scene - the fast-flowing rain-swollen River Worth. Fred was attempting to cross the river on a scattering of semi-submerged moss-covered boulders and large stone blocks to reach the base of the attractive 100 feet tall, stone chimney as he evidently wanted to see where the flue entered the bottom of this most enigmatic mill stack. Whilst I knew that Fred usually didn't care much for watery sites, my attempts to dissuade him about using these stepping stones was not taken. *"I can see t'bottom of the river, Al. It's not that deep, only about eighteen inches"*, exclaimed a much excited Fred.

The main reason, however, for our visit to Low Bridge Mill on this freezing cold morning was for me to show Fred the three intriguing, beautifully carved stone 'human gargoyle' heads set around forty feet high up into the stonework of the chimney above the swirling waters of the River Worth. Despite the fast flowing current, both of us could see that the water would be no higher than to above our knees, so we ventured forth down a slippery and semi-ruinous stone wall and to gain a rather precarious foothold onto the nearest lump of slimy rock which passed as a stepping stone. I was non too keen on rivers either, for I am a poor swimmer, I was therefore, taking my time.

FRED DIBNAH'S CHIMNEY DROPS

**May 1993 Low Bridge Mill, Keighley, with its decorative and highly enigmatic stone chimney.
(Inset) The three carved stone 'human gargoyle' heads set into the chimney.
©Alan McEwen Industrial Heritage Collection**

Fred full of boundless energy and daring-do, surged forward, jumping from stone to stone with his arms stretched out across the icy-cold waters of this Pennine draining beck. *"Eeh Al, it's reet good fun is this, I feel like a kid again".* Fred shouted above the roar of the river, whilst boldly surging forward with a giant leap.

However, misfortune struck. Fred togged up in a green checked woollen shirt, jeans with large turn-ups and his beloved oily cap on his head suddenly slipped off the large boulder he had just landed on and fell backwards into the river. Most normal mortal souls would have been absolutely terrified, but Fred being Fred and blessed with a stout heart and highly athletic with immensely strong arms and muscular ladder-romping legs, just sort of leapt jaguar-like, up and out of the water in a flash and then hauled himself onto some large foundation stones at the chimney base which rose out of the river on the opposite bank.

To my utter amazement, despite Fred being totally saturated, upon him catching his breath and perhaps regaining his composure, he just broke into that special sunshine-laden smile, so very typical of Fred Dibnah and said something like, *"Bloody Hell, Alan, that were a reet lunatic move as I can't swim! The 'Man in the Sky' must be keeping a watch on me".*

After we both had completed a most enjoyable exploration of the chimney with its 'human gargoyles', with chattering teeth we then hauled our frozen bodies up the high stone wall of the river bank; for to be sure, we certainly didn't fancy attempting the haphazard journey back across the river. Upon reaching the wall top which was covered in a thick coating of white hoar frost, and quickly scrambling over, Fred and I then ventured onto the cobble-stone surface of the mill yard which, after briskly crossing, Fred dripping wet, we then reached a pair of battered, much-patched ancient wooden gates where a loose board was swung aside, affording us access to Coney Lane.

HOOLE BANK BRICKWORKS, CHESTER

A half-hour later after motoring back up to Farling Top, we surreptitiously gained access into the Boilerwork's offices where Fred wrung out the majority of water from his clothes, and we both enjoyed a sprucing-up session with hot water. *"Eeh Al, that business of me getting soaked wet through by falling into the river, near t'mill with the fancy chimney in Keighley reminds me of me getting pissed through by falling into a hole in't ground, which could have been my watery grave."* Fred had me in stitches one minute and terrified the very next when he related the following tale:

Fred's story:

HOOLE BANK BRICKWORKS

"This owd lass rang up from a small village near Chester to ask us if we would look at her brickworks chimney stack with a view to knocking it down. The village was called, Mickle Trafford. We set off from Bolton in the Landrover, towing my compressor with all of the tools on board and driving down through Warrington and then carrying on down towards Chester until we finally reached this reet small, but quite pretty village with posh houses and a bonny painted cast iron sign which told us that we had found the village of Mickle Trafford.

I asked a chap passing by if he knew where the owd brickworks were located. He told us it were at Hoole Bank. It weren't far, and when we actually found the site, I found the whole place really very interesting. There were a blacksmith's shop with a massive cast iron forge and a lot of red-rusty tongs. Out back were a mountain of slag and cinders. There were a large Hoffman brick kiln which were quite an interesting building, but looked knackered and had trees sprouting out of the top of it!

A local old guy told me that the site had been used as a brickworks, about thirty or forty years ago. We did a bit of exploring. The chimney that we had come to knock down stood in the middle of a wood, and you couldn't get near to it - the trees were so dense it were like the Burma jungle with millions of pussy willow bushes, birch saplings and elders. At the rear of this site were several old clay pits, filled with water with oil floating on top. A local chap told us that an oil refinery used the clay pits for dumping waste oil. The locals called them lagoons.

For us to get close to the stack to take a gander at the condition of the brickwork, my mate Owd Donald and I had to hack our way through the masses of thorny blackberry bushes, which were growing right thick all around the bottom. After chopping and hacking - all bloody hard graft, we finally got to it and we could see that the bricks were in a very bad state. The brickwork were so badly eroded around the bottom inside of the chimney, that the wall thickness were reduced from two feet thick down to nine inches and the flue had collapsed. The sump were brim-full of green and slimy water which stunk horribly. The brick kiln itself were flooded inside the structure also, like an underground canal, just one big sheet of water, and deep. I didn't like the look of that.

Anyway, we decided we'd do the chimney drop in the usual manner. We'd undermine the base and prop it up on sticks. The thing is, due to the terrible weak state of the chimney base...... the erosion on the inside had partially removed more than half of the thickness of the brick walls...... it were just like a cave inside. The downward pressure from the great, towering weight of brickwork above were bloody terrific. So when you plan to hack out half of it, you will get twice as much weight on the weakened brickwork that is currently holding it up! Extremely dangerous!

I'd decided therefore, that we'd only cut a small hole in the front of the chimney, due to the poor condition it were in. It were in fact, very, very dangerous, and also bloody frightening. We chopped out the opening and propped it with my trusty telegraph pole props and timber cap pieces. We then stacked some dry wood and other combustible rubbish in this here hole, threw a drop o'diesel onto the pile and I then lit it. I then got the C.P.9 airhammer fired up and commenced chiselling brickwork from each side of the bonfire. I thought I were doing awreet. A bit more out on't lefthand side, some more on't reet, the fire were now raging. I thought I'll keep chopping out the bricks steady away like, but the fire were beginning to singe the hairs on the back of me hands. My plan were to keep nibbling away, just until I could see the stack were so fire-ravaged and weakened - and therefore, ready to fall - then I would leg it away at a great speed of knots.

The enormous weight of the 80 feet tall brick chimney pressing down onto the severely burnt and much reduced pit-props is suddenly too much, and the stack topples over.
Ray Willoughby Collection

The chimney dramatically breaks its back.
Ray Willoughby Collection

When you are engaged in demolishing an old chimney by chiselling away at the brickwork, when it's going to fall, you can actually see cracks appearing in the masonry. They open up and run, as you're watching it, before your very eyes. I'm watching, the fire is still burning, the props are about done for and I'm in a deadly situation as the cracks are getting bigger, about a yard long and running vertically up the rotten brickwork. It's time to bloody run!

I've got a grip on me trusty C.P.9 airhammer and had started to back away from the stack, increasing my speed briskly, when all of a sudden, the ground gave way beneath my boots, and I fell down into a bloody great hole about four feet deep and full of stinking, filthy water. Fortunately I landed standing up, the water reached up to my chest height. I were soaked wet through, but I still had a firm grip on my airhammer which I held over the top of my head. I looked up to see a most terrifying image, the knackered old chimney were just about eight feet from where I had plunged into the watery hole, and were now about to commence disintegrating. It all happened in seconds like.

Eeh Alan, how I shot out of yon hole, I'll never know. I were like a bloody rocket coming out of a submarine! All I know is that in my zeal to keep on living, I dropped the airhammer and just sort of sprung up and out of the hole. I ran like the bloody clappers, fear and excitement fuelling me. The roar in my ears as I were running away were bloody incredible. Thankfully, the chimney crashed down in the direction as I had planned, but I didn't see it fall, I just heard an almighty loud rumble as it landed on the deck.

I were soaked to the bloody skin, me right kneecap were badly bruised and I were shaking like a leaf. I were awreet apart from that. After taking a few swigs of cold coffee to strengthen my resolve, I walked back towards the chimney base, following the airline to where I had left it in the water-filled hole. Bloody Hell! Everything were buried in crushed brick. Then the thought struck me. If I hadn't have propelled meself out of yon hole, I would now be dead in a watery grave buried under tons of brickwork."

After listening in awe to Fred's death-defying tale of the Hoole Bank Brickworks chimney drop, I just realised yet again, what a most remarkably brave and very lucky character my friend was.

The falling chimney disappears behind the line of trees.
Ray Willoughby Collection

The aftermath: crushed brick and rubble.
Ray Willoughby Collection

Fred's attractively painted, sign-written trusty Landrover parked in the brickworks yard. To the rear
is the blacksmith's forge building and Fred's mobile diesel compressor.
Ray Willoughby Collection

ARKWRIGHT MILL CHIMNEY DROP, ROCHDALE

Sunday 28th May 1988

The 195 feet tall Arkwright Mill Chimney with Dale Mill to the rear. The whole of Arkwright Mill had been razed to the ground during the redevelopment of the site leaving the chimney standing all alone.
©Alan McEwen Industrial Heritage Collection

It's a pleasantly warm but overcast Sunday morning and I am standing inside the gateway of Arkwright Mill yard answering question after question to an extremely enthusiastic police constable of the Greater Manchester force. I wasn't in trouble, I had in fact recognised Tim the policeman as I had walked past him on entering through the gateway as a youthful acquaintance of many years ago; we had been teenagers together in nearby Middleton. Tim was about my age, and our resultant chat centred around our mutually shared reminiscences of the small, former cotton town, now a part of the modern borough of Rochdale.

Police Constable Tim, was also an ardent admirer of Fred Dibnah and like countless other fans enthused over Fred's television exploits. Tim informed me that he was extremely pleased,

when his sergeant had ordered him, together with about nine other police officers to 'crowd watch' at Fred's Arkwright Mill chimney drop, and the tall, blond-haired, genial police constable was obviously delighted with his posting.

Arkwright Mill was constructed as a five storeyed Accrington brick cotton spinning mill for the Arkwright Spinning Company on Halifax Road, Hamer, a suburb of Rochdale in 1885. The mill engine was built by Petrie & Co. of Rochdale and the three Lancashire boilers were also constructed by Petrie & Co. Arkwright Mill's structure was similar in appearance to numerous other late Victorian-built, red brick mills constructed elsewhere in the cotton towns of Lancashire. Arkwright Mill's circular brick chimney of ubiquitous design was 195 feet high.

FRED DIBNAH'S CHIMNEY DROPS

Fred together with his regular, trusted friend, skilled steeplejack Eddie Chattwood of Ramsbottom had spent the previous week cutting into the brickwork of the chimney base. This 'gobbing out' was carried out to remove approximately a third of the chimney's circumference. Fred and his team of helpers then inserted numerous timber props cut from old telegraph poles which had 'cap-pieces' - sawn from nine inch by three inch thick planks placed on the top of the props into the resulting gap in the brickwork as the chopping out progressed to the lefthand and righthand sides of the vertical start line, which had been chalked on the brickwork. To tighten up the supporting 'pit-props' and 'cap-pieces', long tapering hardwood wedges had been driven between the top of the 'pit-props' and the underside of the 'cap-pieces', thus forming an incredibly strong support structure for the weight of the chimney towering 195 feet tall above.

Fred with hands in pockets of his jacket stands between Arkwright Mill chimney and the neighbouring bulk of Dale Mill; the large bonfire built up of pallets and other scrap timber surround the 'gobbed out' section of the chimney base.
©Alan McEwen Industrial Heritage Collection

On the morning of this chimney drop, I found that due to chatting to Tim, my policeman friend, I had missed out on the 'chimney buffs' regular procedure of collecting and then stacking the old scrap timber to form the bonfire under the pit-props.

"Morning Fred. A good day for the drop", said I, and looking all around me and noticing the burgeoning crowd added, "You've a much bigger crowd than they get at Burnden Park". (Referring to Bolton Wanderers home football ground).

"Aye, it's a bonny big un Al. Let's hope that all these folks go home well pleased", replied Fred. I thought that he looked a trifle nervous. Well who wouldn't be. What a phenomenal amount of responsibility is heaped upon Fred's shoulders, right up until the chimney is safely down on the ground, I pondered.

The bonfire built up from densely stacked timber pallets was enormous and encircled the gobbed opening cut by Fred and Eddie into the chimney base brickwork. It must have been almost ten feet high as well. Noticing that there appeared to be none of the usual scrap lorry tyres in the bonfire, I mentioned this to Fred. *"The Health and Safety Wallahs wouldn't allow us to use them. They're probably frightened that we're gonna burn down Dale Mill"*, said an exasperated Fred jerking his right thumb in the direction of the nearby bulk of Dale Mill. *"They're like bloody rabbits, frightened to death of everything that has a lot of danger and excitement involved. There's a safety officer over there, telling the coppers on where he wants the crowd to stand. Probably half a mile away"*, he added, pointing out a small, grey-suited, pale-complexioned chap in a trilby.

At 11.15 a.m. precisely, Fred instructed a woman to light the bonfire with a torch improvised from a length of wood with a rag nailed on to one end of it and soaked in diesel-fuel oil. Within minutes of the lighting, the mountainous bone-dry stack of wooden pallets were well alight and blazing furiously. From my location at the extreme top end of the mill yard where I had set up my Olympus cameras, I could see the flames being dramatically sucked into the 'gobbed-out' breech, and I could hear the distinctive whistling and roaring sounds of the gases of combustion racing up the tall brick chimney. Black coils of smoke lifted skywards.

These chimney drops of Fred's were extremely friendly affairs; friendships were struck with like-minded individuals, people who were interested in Britain's industrial history, chimney-buffs: mainly youngish middle-aged men who came to meet Fred and take perhaps scores of photographs, and not least the regular small but dedicated band, both male and female, who were close friends of Fred. I was proud to be a member of this band.

Left: With the fire burning ferociously around the pit-props supporting the 195 feet tall chimney, the sky is darkened with large plumes of inky black smoke issuing out of the chimney top.
©Alan McEwen Industrial Heritage Collectio

Some 35 minutes following the lighting of the fire the chimney falls.
©Alan McEwen Industrial Heritage Collection

FRED DIBNAH'S CHIMNEY DROPS

It's now 11.50, and from my vantage point, I could just about make out the line of thin, bent and considerably weakened timber props as the massive bonfire had burned down. I then heard Fred's Klaxon horn sound its distinctive death knell tone for the stricken Arkwright Mill chimney. Fred then shouts, "its gawin". The 195 foot chimney suddenly topples as though in slow motion. All around me, the regiment of chimney buffs and onlookers take a multitude of photographs. A massive cheer goes up followed by hearty clapping. The chimney falls and strikes the hard, compacted surface of the mill yard with great violence. We, the crowd of chimney enthusiasts, and general public alike are covered in eye-stinging dust and smoke. I could hear a man coughing close by. A little boy is crying; he has a speck of dirt in his eye. His mother tenderly wipes the poorly eye with a Kleenex. Its over! Another chimney bites the dust.

Minutes after the fall a fascinated police constable studies the brick rubble, all that now remains of the Arkwright Mill chimney whilst being shunted by a bulldozer.
©Alan McEwen Industrial Heritage Collection

When the dust and smoke clears, all that now remains of the chimney is a long mound of smoking, crushed brick; iron bands poke up through this mass. I then see Fred who is surrounded with well-wishers. "You've done a brilliant job Fred", shouts a bald man. Master steeplejack and television personality Fred Dibnah poses for the cameras after clambering on top of the heaps of bricks. With his typically wide and sunny smile, he shouts to his admiring fans, *"Did yer like that?".*

A few minutes later when the crowd had dispersed a little, I joined up with Fred. "That drop was fantastic, well done Fred mate", said I. *"Thanks Al, but its sad, another one down",* replied Fred quietly. He was however, back to his usual confident and cheerful self, but I could sense that he was relieved now the chimney was no more.

Following the chimney drop, our small band of close friends of Fred motored over to his house at Bolton to celebrate, the efficient and profoundly safe Arkwright Mill chimney drop.

The front end view of Fred's workhorse, his trusty Landrover. The author stands to the left complete with boilersuit and flat cap.
©Alan McEwen Industrial Heritage Collection

This image shows Fred cheerfully hauling in the copper lightning conductor from out of the mass of crushed brick rubble.
©Alan McEwen Industrial Heritage Collection

Lancashire Hill Mill Chimney Drop, Stockport.

Sunday 2nd April 1989

Lancashire Hill Mill, Stockport. The superb 180 feet tall, octagonal, brick chimney with its distinctive ornamented oversiller was photographed just two hours before Fred Dibnah's demolition on 2nd April 1989.
©Alan McEwen Industrial Heritage Collection

It was very cold, and a mixture of sleet and rain was falling on the Sunday morning of the 2nd of April 1989 as I was trundling in my Isuzu Trooper along the busy, traffic-choked A6 in Manchester, heading down to Stockport to witness and hopefully take part in another of Fred Dibnah's amazing chimney felling jobs at Lancashire Hill Mill.

After driving through Levenshulme, and upon passing the biscuit factory on my right, I could feel the 'sap' rising in my body; the sheer thrill and intense excitement of the forthcoming dramatic event always made me react like this. I just loved every minute of Fred's chimney demolition jobs. For I was truly in heaven when drinking in the 'special atmosphere' that pervade these old mill sites. It was like a drug; a fix.

I found it exhilarating, exciting: a mixture of intense excitement, laced with profound danger, and tremendous respect for my friend Fred's skills in engineering precisely the felling of the chimney to drop exactly as planned. I also felt, very much like Fred, profound sadness too, for these chimneys were masterpieces of the Victorian mill-builders art. They had served Britain well, and now they were no longer required, 'no longer loved' as Fred eloquently put it, and therefore, had to be demolished and cleared away.

On reaching Lancashire Hill, I could see a short distance ahead, the tall latticework steel jib of the demolition company's crane towering above a block of time-blackened brick mill buildings. I pulled off the Manchester Road down a cobbled, mean-looking street and into the mill yard, where I then safely parked the Isuzu Trooper several hundred feet away from the demolition activities. I had previously carried out a little research into the history of Lancashire Hill Mill, which revealed that it had been built as a cotton spinning manufactory by Thomas Rivett in 1887, passing into the ownership of Joseph Rivett and Sons in 1897 and being known as the Lancashire Hill Thread Works. The business was subsequently taken over by The Fine Cotton Spinners and Doublers Association.

The wind had picked up driving sleet flurries hither, thither and the temperature was dropping rapidly. Fred most definitely would not be pleased with the strength of the wind, I thought. Prior to walking across the mill yard to where the 180 feet tall, octagonal brick chimney was sited, I decided, that as I was on site a good hour earlier than planned, I may as well do a little bit of exploring hereabouts.

I walked over to the rear of the yard where there was a substantial brick wall which divided the mill site from the canal towpath on the other side. I then noticed that a section of the wall had been damaged, resulting in it being reduced from its original height of about twelve feet into a pile of rubble. Walking over to this mound, I could look down into the Stockport Canal, the surface of the water being partially frozen into sheets of ice. Clambering atop the mound of bricks, I attained a birds eye view across the canal of the decomposing millscapes that fanned out towards Stockport town centre. "Hells Teeth", I muttered. "This area of Stockport must have been an industrial powerhouse". I retraced my steps back to the Isuzu to collect my Olympus camera and to find Fred.

Thomas Rivett's Lancashire Hill Thread Works letterhead dated 20th May 1884.
Courtesy of Stockport Library of Local Studies

A delightful characteristic image of Master Steeplejack Fred Dibnah posing proudly beneath the Lancashire Hill Mill chimney prior to demolition.
Chris Hill Collection.

However, Fred found me first. *"Hiya cock. Despite this bloody awful weather you've made it then. I bet its ten foot deep in snow up on them Yorkshire moors where you live"*, said Fred *"Int it bloody windy?, I just wish t'wind would settle down. It can be reet bloody scary tha knows, bein' close to a big chimney with the bumfire rapidly burning away the pit-props. The wind can play havoc with the chimney drop. You can't always guarantee if the sodding chimney will actually fall, the fire might have burnt out, leaving the stack standing, but sort of trembling like, due to the wind. Reet deadly stuff".* *"At least the damned sleet has stopped"*, I cheerfully replied. We both walked towards the tall, octagonal brick stack, which still retained its most attractive, large and ornate oversiller.

"What a bonny chimney Fred. It's a tragedy that it is to be felled" said I. *"Aye, poor bugger is no longer loved. As you know Alan, I don't like knocking 'em down either, but I've got to live. If I don't knock 'em down, then some other guy will. T'demolition contractor was going to blow it up, but the bigwigs from the health and safety wouldn't let them. This is how I got the job. They seem to trust me with my sticks and bumfire routine. It's bloody sad, but it's got to go".*

Fred and his mates had carried out the 'gobbing out' process earlier that week and I counted over twenty stout timber props supporting the towering mass of masonry that soared 180 feet above. The square brickwork chimney base had at some time in its life been spray-can daubed with Anglo-Saxon profanities and weird hieroglyphics. Very photogenic!

With just a half-hour to spare before the ceremonial lighting of the demolition bonfire, I got stuck in with Fred and other acquaintances enthusiastically stacking timber and old lorry tyres amongst the pit-props holding up the chimney.

On the morning of the drop, Fred and fellow steeplejack Eddie Chattwood are hard at work boring holes into the pit props. These holes assist the flames to rapidly consume the timber. Notice to the left hand side the original flue. Fred's old Landrover workhorse, his 'Lanny' is parked to the rear.
©Alan McEwen Industrial Heritage Collection

Surrounded by a bizarre collection of graffiti daubed onto the brickwork of the chimney base, Fred can be seen calculating the load of the towering masonry upon the pit props with his trammel points.
©Alan McEwen Industrial Heritage Collection

Fred's second wife Susan, ignited the Lancashire Hill Mill's chimney funeral pyre at bang on 11 o'clock. Notwithstanding the rain-soaked bonfire material, the flames soon took hold, the strong wind inducing the flames up into the chimney's throat. Thick, black smoke issued out from the doomed chimney's decorative top. From my safe vantage point behind a massive steel demolition contractor's skip sited several hundreds of feet away from the chimney, I could hear the fire roaring within the barrel.

The scene is set. The bonfire has been built under the chimney. Most of the on-lookers have moved to a safe position whilst a number of brave young souls can be seen milling about in the actual path of the chimney drop.
©Alan McEwen Industrial Heritage Collection

LANCASHIRE HILL MILL, STOCKPORT

I glanced at my watch, 11.15 a.m. I couldn't see Fred for he was located at the rear of the chimney base, undoubtedly watching carefully for the tell-tale cracks that heralded the fall. I fired off several shots with my Olympus. "Parp, parp.....parp" Fred's airhorn. Hells teeth its going over. A split second later and I noticed the chimney buckle, then lean in what appeared to be 'slow motion', then over it went to crash onto the wet yard with an almighty roar. It had taken just sixteen and a half minutes from the lighting of the bonfire for the mighty 102 year old chimney to fall. The whole demolition of the stack had been expertly carried out by Fred and all that remained was a smouldering mountain of brick rubble fanning out in a precise path, exactly as Fred had calculated.

Later, I spoke with Alan Johnson, a director of Reddish Demolition Limited, whom Fred was working for. Alan was clearly delighted with Fred's safe and efficient felling of the chimney. "It was a spectacular performance which really brought the house down" he said. He explained that his company had been refused permission to blow down the chimney with explosives by their insurance company and due to Fred's unrivalled reputation regarding safe and efficient working practices, his firm had placed a contract with the famous steeplejack. So despite the awful weather conditions, the Lancashire Hill Mill chimney drop went extremely well. The huge rain-soaked crowd of Fred's admirers that had boldly attended gave Fred a resounding cheer and he was clearly delighted.

Across a wilderness of brick rubble and smashed concrete the bonfire can be seen blazing furiously; black smoke issues forth from the decorative chimney top.
©Alan McEwen Industrial Heritage Collection

Fred with his beloved, trusty air operated klaxon.
Chris Hill Collection.

Just 16½ minutes after the bonfire was lit the chimney was no more.
Chris Hill Collection.

During the afternoon our close-knit band of chimney buffs and friends celebrated the event in the time-honoured fashion by supping a few Guinnesses at Fred's home, back in Bolton.

A triumphant Fred poses for photographers on a mountain of brick rubble, all that now remains of the Lancashire Hill Mill chimney.
©Alan McEwen Industrial Heritage Collection

LANGHO HOSPITAL CHIMNEY DROP, NR. WHALLEY, LANCASHIRE

Sunday 13th January 1990

The Langho Hospital chimney and the few remaining hospital buildings amidst the organised chaos of the demolition site.
©Alan McEwen Industrial Heritage Collection

On my arrival on the old Langho hospital site, I discovered that all of the buildings had been totally demolished and cleared except for a squat red brick building with a raised glazed roof, which apparently was the Power House, together with a small cluster of ancillary buildings. The Langho Hospital site was located out in the countryside adjacent to the A59 Preston–Skipton road, about 2½ miles from Ribchester and set amidst beautiful, well-cared for grounds with an abundance of mature trees, and shrubberies. My visit was in mid-winter, I imagined that in the summer the whole area would be breathtakingly beautiful.

The attractive 120 feet tall brick chimney, from a distance, appeared to be square in section, but as I got close up, I could then easily discern that it was actually octagonal, the facets consisting of four wide sections, and another four angled corner sections being considerably narrow in width. The stack rose up in the air gracefully and adding to its attractiveness was the stone mouldings of the transitional section between the squat base and the chimney's shaft proper; there were several bands of stone interspersing the brickwork, terminating in a bonny little oversiller, also of stone. It was indeed a most pleasing little chimney.

The author's 7 year old son Alasdair poses for camera in front of the chimney, which has been previously 'gobbed out' and 'pit-propped' in readiness for dropping. To the front of the chimney base, heaps of scrap wood, old pallets and old lorry tyres await stacking against the 'pit-props' which, when completed will form the bonfire. To the rear right hand side of the picture, Fred can be seen coupling compressed air pipes to his mobile diesel compressor which is still hitched to the rear of his distinctive lettered Landover.
©Alan McEwen Industrial Heritage Collection

Fred, assisted by a friendly 'chimney buff', drills holes through the timber 'pit-props' that support the weight of the chimney.
©Alan McEwen Industrial Heritage Collection

The day was extremely cold with icy drizzle falling and was exceedingly wet and slippery underfoot. The ground around the chimney site had originally been the floor of the hospital's basement and on all sides were mountainous heaps of smashed brick and concrete, twisted steel girders and pulverised timber that remained uncleared.

Fred and a friendly 'chimney buff' could be viewed hard at work drilling holes into the timber 'pit-props' with the Consolidated Pneumatic air drill, whilst another member of Fred's team, steeplejack Eddie Chattwood was busy filling up several buckets with diesel fuel oil from a trailer-mounted bowser tank. The diesel was to be used as an accelerant to make the bonfire burn faster.

By 11.30 a.m. in spite of the perishing cold, which, unless you kept busy by moving around the site caused you to continuously shiver, I could see that Fred and his mate had completed the drilling and was indicating to the small band of cheerful 'chimney buffs', myself included, that we could now commence with the building of the bonfire. So, with much light-hearted banter our small, yet dedicated band of chimney enthusiasts, proceeded to collect the multifarious waste material: old timber, wooden pallets, roof beams, plastic crates and a couple of dozen car and lorry tyres, which was then carefully piled around the 'pit-props' under the 'gobbed out' opening in the chimney base.

Fred with his typically friendly, cheerful manner, then proceeded to instruct us where to place the bonfire materials around the gob. Harry, a fellow chimney buff and yours truly were struggling to roll a monster tractor tyre into place, when Fred seeing that we needed some aid, quickly assisted us in rolling the extremely heavy tyre up along the bonfire stack whilst saying, "lets s*tick yon tyre in theer lads,*" as he gestured to one of the 'glory holes' within the chimney bonfire. *"Aye reet, that's smashing"*. *"That will make the bonfire blaze"* he cheerfully added.

"When did you and Eddie commence with the 'gobbing out", I asked Fred, whilst he offered me two polo mints clenched between an oil-stained finger and thumb. *"Er, Wednesday morning, but the bloody weather, it's been really cold. It's much colder here than down in Bolton",* replied Fred, whilst rubbing his frozen hands together to coax some life back into them. Looking around, I realised that the other chaps had completed the building of the bonfire which was to be lit, by Sue, Fred's wife, at 12 o'clock.

I then moved off to wander around the demolition site in an attempt to kill the few remaining minutes whilst keyed up as ever with rising excitement for Fred's chimney drop event at mid-day. I made my way over to the Power House to shelter from the inclement weather, where I met a well-dressed gentleman and entered into a pleasant conversation with him. Mr. Jones, I'll call him, was a local retired businessman and a keen local historian, and it was he that related to me the 'potted history' of the Langho Hospital.

The Hospital site, which until the demolition, had in recent times been a nursing home for elderly people, but had originally been known as the Langho Colony and had been built in 1904/6 by the Poor Law Guardians as an institution for sufferers of epilepsy, then called 'the falling sickness'. Langho's patients came from all over Lancashire with the majority coming up from Manchester. Langho Colony consisted in the early 20th century of villas, workshops and buildings for the administration and recreation on an estate extending to almost 200 acres. It was situated in beautiful unspoilt country with views of Pendle Hill and Longridge Fell and flanked by its own farms, with the Lancashire and Yorkshire Railway running behind the site. It was then totally secluded from the outside world.

There were six homes grouped into male and female villages. There were also sixteen more buildings known as 'colony buildings', that included an administrative block, an assembly hall which doubled as a chapel; kitchens, a steam laundry, workshops and a Power House which generated electricity from a reciprocating steam engine. There was a Boiler House containing a number of steam boilers which provided heating for the entire hospital and steam power for the reciprocating steam engine. The chimney was built nearby to provide the necessary draught for the steam boilers. There was also a mortuary, a porters' lodge and a substantial house for the Langho Colony's Superintendent. The building contractors were Robert Neil and Sons of Manchester, a well established and respected firm who had built Crumpsall Infirmary in Manchester in 1876, and several other hospitals including the mental institution, Winwick Asylum. The building of Langho Colony proceeded throughout 1904, 1905 and 1906, the total cost being around £100,000. The opening ceremony on the 3rd of September 1906 was carried out with pomp by the Earl of Derby, Lord Lieutenant of Lancashire.

Fred expertly pokes the mass of blazing timber to encourage it to blaze fiercely. The crowd of onlookers, many with umbrellas view the scene from a safe distance.
©Alan McEwen Industrial Heritage Collection

I bade farewell to my new and most informative friend Mr. Jones, and with my head buzzing with a multitude of building specifications, cost figures and historical data, I then moved down across the demolition site to the chimney base with only just two or three minutes to spare before the lighting of the chimney's funeral pyre.

With the freezing-light rain still falling from a leaden sky, at 12 o'clock on the dot, Susan Dibnah lit the bonfire, which soon burst into flame aided by several buckets full of diesel being hurled over the burning combustible materials by Fred and Eddie. Soon, gigantic flames roared skywards and as the insides of the chimney reached high temperature, long tongues of orangey flames were sucked through 'the gob' and up the throat of the chimney shaft that created a loud roaring noise. Massive wraiths of pitch-black smoke uncoiled from the chimney top to cover the demolition site and surrounding woodland with choking smog. From my eerie, high up on a pile of heaped brick and concrete, where I had perched with my cameras and tripods, I had a bird's eye view of the bonfire which, within around 15 minutes of the lighting was rapidly reducing to matchsticks, the pit-props supporting the bulk of the chimney. My instinct told me that the Langho Hospital chimney would

not stand much longer.

At twenty-one minutes into the burn, suddenly Fred's klaxon sounded the chimney's impending fall. I watched transfixed, as the 120 feet tall, graceful brick stack suddenly stirred from its foundations and dramatically fell, its barrel breaking into three or four sections before it struck the ground with an almighty crash. Fred's supportive crowd of 'chimney buffs' and locals, uttered a tumultuous cheer followed by much clapping of frozen hands and stamping of chilled feet together with the usual whistles.

On joining Fred's side, I congratulated my close friend, "a brilliant drop Fred. Well done mate", said I. *"I knew that it would be a good un, we'd engineered it just reet Al"*, Fred buoyantly replied, his white teeth lighting up his grime-stained sooty countenance.

Then it was off to a local pub to get out of the appalling weather and to assist Fred with his Langho Hospital chimney dropping celebrations with pints of Guinness and Lancashire bitter all round.

The fire is now burning ferociously and black smoke pours from out of the chimney top.
©Alan McEwen Industrial Heritage Collection

With the fire-ravaged 'pit-props' no longer being able to support the enormous weight pressing
down from above, they suddenly collapse, and the chimney falls.......
©Alan McEwen Industrial Heritage Collection

..........and down it crashed onto the ground.
©Alan McEwen Industrial Heritage Collection

What a grand result, however sad; all that remains of the Langho Hospital chimney is a
mountainous pile of broken bricks. Steeplejack Eddie Chattwood moves
in to retrieve the valuable copper lightning conductor.
©Alan McEwen Industrial Heritage Collection

BANK VALE PAPERMILL CHIMNEY DROP, HAYFIELD, DERBYSHIRE

Sunday 8th November 1990

The Bank Vale Paper Mill chimney with the large expectant crowd starting to assemble in this delightful location amidst the rolling north Derbyshire hills.
©Alan McEwen Industrial Heritage Collection

I had been particularly looking forward to this chimney drop ever since Fred had cordially invited me during one of my regular fortnightly visits to his yard around mid- October. Fred's colourful description of the Paper Mill site as being 'marooned out in the wilds' of the High Peak District, near Glossop, I found immensely appealing, for I was reasonably acquainted with the cotton town of Glossop and also its neighbouring villages such as Dinting, Chunel and the small delightfully named village close to where the chimney was sited, Hayfield.

During the late 1960s and early 1970s, I had enjoyed working in a goodly number of the cotton mills and factories hereabouts, wherein I had carried out repairs to many venerable Lancashire boilers, rag-boiling Kiers and even several vertical crosstube boilers.

I found the dramatic scenery of this part of north Derbyshire, an intoxicating mix of rugged, stone-built townscapes and ancient, former cotton spinning semi-industrial villages all tightly ram-jam packed into the valley bottoms; the enigmatic industrial architecture and moreover, the surrounding high windswept hills; 'the Peaks' with their boundless acres of ling and heather covered fellsides, scattered clumps of wind-twisted Hawthorn and Blackthorn, and numerous clear, babbling brooks that drain the fells -- all truly spellbinding.

Prior to the day of Fred's chimney drop at Bank Vale Paper Mill, I had invited my old friend John Brooks and also his wife Jean and daughter Adele to accompany my family and I to the chimney demolition at Hayfield. John was an accomplished mechanical and steam engineer and worked for a large and nationally renowned specialist steam equipment manufacturer based in the south west. John and I had worked on numerous steam related projects in boiler houses all over northern England ever since the early 1970s and we were both firm friends.

Like thousands of other people, John was an ardent admirer of Fred Dibnah and thoroughly enjoyed his television programmes. On several occasions, John had asked me if he could join up with me during one of my visits to Fred's home. Unfortunately, a mutually convenient time was never reached, due to other business and work-related commitments. Therefore, a visit to Fred's yard for John was never achieved which made me feel quite troubled. However, this time it was going to be different, my old friend John was most definitely going to meet my famous old friend Fred Dibnah, and when I invited him, John was clearly over the moon.

The Sunday of the chimney drop was one of those lovely late autumn days when the sun lights up the countryside in a golden hue. We set off from Farling Top in two cars, my family and I in my Isuzu Trooper and John Brooks, his wife Jean and daughter Adele in their car following at the rear.

The journey down to Glossop took just over an hour, and was spent with me waxing lyrical about the large numbers of weaving sheds, cotton mills and skywards thrusting chimneys that we passed en route. Entering the town I pointed out a large chemical works, where my firm had once retubed a huge packaged boiler and also the gigantic riveted iron railway bridge carrying the Manchester to Sheffield trans-Pennine railway high across the road. Another four miles along twisting, hilly country roads and we arrived in the beautiful hamlet of Brooksbottom, perhaps a couple of miles distant from Hayfield.

As Fred had taken great pains to describe the exact location of Bank Vale Paper Mill, I recognised it as soon as I saw it from my car. On stopping the car, I noticed far down in the valley bottom to my right, a large meadow surrounded with dry stone walling and sited close to the edge of the field, I could see a tall stone chimney rising high above a clutch of mill buildings with flagstone roofs that nestled further down into the valley bottom. I could also see that a large crowd had gathered around the chimney. This was it. We were at Bank Vale Paper Mill. How exciting.

The surrounding Derbyshire countryside, despite it being late autumn was still quite lush and green. Cows munched the sweet meadow grass and countless sheep could be seen high up on the steeply sloping fellsides

After parking our cars in an adjacent field which was acting as a temporary car park, and pointing out to our families a good viewing area for the forthcoming excitement, John and I set off trudging our way downhill through a small copse of oak, beech and ash, the colours of the leaves ranged from yellow through red and purple, and the light breeze caused cascades of beautiful coloured leaves to rain down onto us. The meadow was exceedingly wet underfoot with liquid mud and cow pats splashing all over our boots and jeans as we made a beeline for the chimney. However, as we got closer to the octagonal shaped stack which was built of blackened Millstone Grit, and about a hundred feet high, the field became much drier, which made our progress that much easier. Nevertheless, our jeans were caked in mud and cow muck.

As we approached the chimney I saw the characteristic flat-capped figure of Fred at the chimney base enthusiastically explaining to a gathering of his fans who all appeared to be attired in their Sunday best, the technicalities of 'gobbing out', of 'pit-propping' the towering mass of the condemned chimney, and other campanological procedures.

Quietly and cheerily pushing our way through the throng, we approached Fred from the left hand side. "Morning Fred. Can I introduce an old friend of mine? John this is Fred. Fred this is John. He's a steam engineer, specialising in steam traps and other highly technical steamy contraptions". Fred and John shook hands. *"Welcome to Bank Vale Paper Mill both of you"*, said a smiling Fred.

"Steam traps did you say Alan, I could do with a big bucket-type steam trap to drain my Weir steam pump". Turning to John, Fred inquired if John's firm supplied good quality, second-hand steam traps. John appeared somewhat bemused. "Er, er, we don't supply any used products whatsoever", replied my friend to Fred. "However, I'll see what I can do about obtaining a bucket-trap at a vastly reduced cost". Fred was clearly pleased.

FRED DIBNAH'S CHIMNEY DROPS

Left: The bonfire materials have been stacked within the gobbed-out chimney base. Numerous chimney buffs and Fred's fans assemble around the base.
©Alan McEwen Industrial Heritage Collection

I had noticed that the demolition bonfire material consisting of scrap wood, old tyres and sheets of tarred roofing felt had been previously stacked around the pit-props at the 'gobbed out' section of the chimney base. My involvement on this occasion was therefore, not required.

John and I ambled our way back uphill to where our respective families were grouped beneath a large and ancient gnarled Hawthorn bush. We were delighted for we all had a most superb view of the chimney from our elevated location high up on the steep slope of the valley side. Both of my children, Alasdair and Shonagh were very excited, and so too was John's daughter Adele.

With the fire burning furiously, great swathes of black smoke pour out from the chimney top to sully the beautiful surrounding autumn Derbyshire countryside.
©Alan McEwen Industrial Heritage Collection

BANK VALE PAPERMILL, HAYFIELD

We all had been patiently waiting for the allotted bonfire lighting time of 11.30 a.m., when a distant church bell tolled the half hour. It was 11.30 a.m. dead on the dot. From our high vantage point, looking down, we could see Fred instructing a young lad to push the blazing firebrand he held in his hands into the bonfire. Within less than a minute - whoosh, the wood quickly ignited, due no doubt, I guessed, to several buckets of diesel oil having drenched the bonfire stack, just prior to lighting.

Within a couple of minutes more and the bonfire was burning furiously. Long gouts of flame were being sucked into the 'gobbed-out' opening in the chimney base. Thick, black smoke belched out of the chimney top and blanketed the whole of the bottom of the valley swirling in great, black clouds around the old paper mill buildings lower down.

I glanced at my watch. It registered 11.36 a.m. The bonfire was by now blazing furiously, the flames consuming the timber pit-props. My experienced ears could make out the distinctive sound of stones exploding from high up within the chimney's barrel, due to the high internal temperatures and to cascade down onto the fire. My thoughts were that the chimney had become significantly weaker.

Within eight minutes of the fire being lit, Fred's air horn could be heard all over the site sounding the death knell of this old stone stack as it commenced its fall.
©Alan McEwen Industrial Heritage Collection

Suddenly, a shout of warning from Fred could be clearly heard followed by four loud blasts of his beloved air horn. Hell's Teeth, the chimney was toppling. True enough, the old stone stack, severely ravaged by the action of the high temperature flames, suddenly buckled and then dramatically crashed to the ground with an almighty roar. An enormous dust storm swirled around the site mixed with inky black smoke. Just eight minutes following the lighting of the bonfire, the once proudly standing chimney was no more. It was now just a long snake of crushed and pulped stone prostrated upon the grassy hillside. The large crowd of mainly local people whooped with delight; Fred had served them well, he'd given them a Sunday to remember. Fred was thereafter, for well over an hour, surrounded by well wishers and fans, many requesting him to autograph books, pose for photographs, or to just chat with the cheerful, amiable steeplejack from Bolton.

I went over and congratulated Fred, who cheerily stated, that the Bank Vale Paper Mill chimney drop had been timed and recorded as being eight minutes from the lighting of the fire to the actual drop and was evidently therefore, a record. A triumphant first for Fred; one of many firsts for Fred's future.

To celebrate, the McEwens and Brooks families enjoyed a wonderful lunch in a lovely old stone pub in Hayfield village centre.

Later that evening, I called at Fred's house, Park Cottage in Bolton and enjoyed a chat with him and a bottle or two of Guinness in his Engine Shed.

With the massive raging inferno at the chimney base the once proud Bank Vale Paper Mill chimney falls.
©Alan McEwen Industrial Heritage Collection

The author with Fred and fellow enthusiast Frank Hardman, stand with their backs against the Dibnah workhorse. Note the scaffolding poles that form a carrying platform for Fred's ladders and planks all securely connected to the Landrover.
©Alan McEwen Industrial Heritage Collection

Whitfield Mill Chimney Drop
Millfold, Facit,
Near Rochdale

Sunday 25th November 1990

The distinctive square stone Whitfield Mill Chimney rears above the semi derelict surrounding mill buildings and was typical of numerous chimneys once found in the Whitworth Valley.
©*Alan McEwen Industrial Heritage Collection*

FRED DIBNAH'S CHIMNEY DROPS

Located high in the Whitworth Valley betwixt Rochdale and Bacup in the small Pennine hamlet of Facit, once a hive of industrial activity with scores of cotton spinning mills tightly packed onto the bottom of the valley and abandoned stone quarries, was the decaying bulk of Whitfield Mill with its attendant 160 feet tall, square-section chimney constructed from massively hewn blocks of Millstone Grit and the local iron-hard Haslingden Flagstone.

It was late November 1990, Fred Dibnah and his long-serving friend Mick had previously commenced with 'gobbing out', the process involving cutting a hole into the stonework base of the Whitfield Mill chimney and propping with old sections of telegraph poles when Fred gave me a call on the 'phone. *"Hello, hello Al, my mate Mick is buggering off for a couple of days, so do you think you could escape from your boiler-making activities and give me a hand preparing a bloody monster stone chimney dropping?"* My old friend Fred requested.

Fred and his mate Mick hard at work rock-drilling through the massive blocks of Millstone Grit whilst 'gobbing out'. The huge bulk of the 160 foot high stone stack with its many iron corsets that strengthen the masonry, rises high above the men.
©Alan McEwen Industrial Heritage Collection

WHITFIELD MILL, FACIT, NR. ROCHDALE

Close-up of Fred 'gobbing out' down the right hand side of the stone stack.
©Alan McEwen Industrial Heritage Collection

"Where's the chimney located Fred"? I enquired with rising anticipation of good things to come. *"A spot up int' mountains above Rochdale called Facit, a reet bloody cowd and draughty hole called Whitfield Mill"* replied Fred. With excitement coursing through the whole of my body at the prospect of me working with the nation's most renowned master steeplejack, my good friend Fred Dibnah, after giving him a resounding "aye, I'd be delighted to assist", and after enjoying the usual lengthy chat on the 'phone and then bidding Fred goodnight, I couldn't wait for the following day. How exciting!

The following morning at 6.30 a.m. when I set off in my trusty red Bedford CF diesel truck, it was perishing cold with much evidence of Jack Frost having laid his freezing, white sparkling carpet on the still dark moorland surrounding Farling Top. The road surface was covered in black ice all the way up the steep moorland road over 'Cowling

Moss' on the Lancashire-Yorkshire border but driving steadily once over the watershed and into Lancashire where the roads had been salted the driving got easier. I continued downhill and along the A6068 through the small, attractive Pennine town of 'bonnie' Colne, then on through Burnley passing several dead but very attractive candlestick chimneys alongside the massive old cotton mills.

I climbed up the Bacup road out of Burnley and passed Towneley Hall, and then tackled the long hard climb up to Deerplay which stands at an elevated position surrounded with wild moorland on the old turnpike between Rochdale and Burnley at an elevation of well over 1100 feet. I then let the Bedford roll down to pass through the desolate moorland village called Weir, thence rolling all the way down the sinuous road, passing Broadclough Mills with its square stone chimneys; I imagined Fred's Whitfield Mill chimney would look like these.

I was enjoying myself even though it was freezing cold I drove with the cab window wide open for I was well wrapped up and used to Pennine winters. With the River Irwell on my left hand side the street lights of the old cotton town of Bacup welcomed me. Bacup with its numerous mills is jam-packed into a bowl-like depression surrounded by high bleak moorland. A mile or so up the tortuous winding Rochdale road brought me into the hilltop village of Britannia. One or two people could be seen heads down in thick heavy overcoats on the way to work in the local factories. I drove passed the distinctive old blackened stone mill still emblazoned with the firm's name in white paint, 'The Lancashire Sock Company' with its lovely chimney, thence forwards downhill to enter the Whitworth Valley. Another couple of miles passing many old, and interesting mills, chimneys standing like lonesome sentinels dotted here and there, and the remains of long abandoned quarries scarring the surrounding Pennine fell sides, on entering the hamlet of Facit I then turned right in front of the crumbling edifice of the incongruous red brick and terracotta Facit Mill to enter Millfold and into Whitfield Mill yard.

By golly I was thrilled, diving out of my truck and looking up, even though it was still dark I could make out the 160 feet tall, tapering chimney rising up above the few surviving cotton mill buildings to dominate the whole of Millfold. I could also hear the unmistakable sound of a powerful pneumatic rock drill hard at work. Rounding the corner of the mill, I then espied Fred hard at work, enthusiastically and expertly drilling and cutting into the stubborn and unyielding masonry at the foot of the chimney. I walked up behind him and lightly tapped him on his right shoulder. He swung round to face me, easing back the trigger on the rock drill. *"Hi Al, thanks for coming over"*, and pointing into the maw of the 'gobbed out' section of the chimney he informed me in colourful language, *"that the bloody infill is constructed from that hard stuff, Haslingden Flagstone. Its bloody terrible material to drill and cut and it's blunting my chisels and also buggering me up an' all"*.

This study shows the front right hand corner of the chimney secured with pit-props and cap pieces. Fred is busily engaged in the bowels of the chimney base breaking out and removing the iron-hard Haslingden Flagstone infill. Obviously an exceedingly dangerous task.
©Alan McEwen Industrial Heritage Collection

Fred and Mick cutting old telegraph poles to make into the pit-props needed to shore up the 'gobbed out' sections of the chimney's masonry.
©Alan McEwen Industrial Heritage Collection

Close up showing Fred rock drilling the chimney base core material amongst the pit-props. Fred quipped to the author *"its just like bloody mining!"*
©Alan McEwen Industrial Heritage Collection

With my enthusiasm knowing no bounds I offered Fred a hand. "Let me give you a spell on the drill", I ventured. I was used to the weight, the power and the ear-splitting noise of all types of compressed air tools, as we used them in the boiler-making industry. Fred was correct, for despite the powerful rock drill, I found that after about a half an hour of drilling out the iron-hard masonry, I was sweating cobs, covered in thick grey dust, and shaking like a leaf with the exertion of holding the drill with both arms whilst either crouching into the gobbed opening or lying on my side. Despite me sweating profusely, it was still below freezing and the wind had picked up bringing snow flurries all of which made me work harder.

Subsequent to the chiselling out of the stone and shovelling the rubble to one side, Fred motioned for me to have a breather, whilst he drove in one of his pine (former telegraph pole) props and cap pieces cut from old planks to hold up the massive weight of the chimney towering above us. Thus, we advanced 'gobbing out' across the frontal flat side and then round into both sides of the chimney.

After chomping on a Whitworth bacon-filled muffin washed down with a pint mug of scalding hot, refreshing tea, Fred enthusiastically showed me around the mill site and pointed out the extremely narrow slot for his planned chimney fall which was between a rake of empty offices and a cottage on the left-hand side and a partially filled in mill lodge on the right. A dangerously narrow chimney dropping slot! Standing at the side of the quarry waste-filled lodge, Fred commenced to tell me a rather intriguing tale that he himself had heard from an old chap who lived close by and who had wondered into the mill yard to chat to Fred several days previously. Very excitedly, Fred told me the story as related by the old chap, that evidently the mill lodge had never been fully drained and apparently just following the period of the First World War, the mill management owned a horse-drawn steam fire engine, either a Merryweather or a Shand-Mason that had suffered serious boiler trouble, too costly to repair, and therefore had became redundant and in the way. Instead of scrapping this engine, the powers that be, had it disposed of by pushing it into the mill lodge that had by then fell into disuse.

Several decades later, when the mill company required parking space for cars and lorries, the lodge had been 'filled in' by the tipping of several tons of waste rock rubble from a local quarry. Fred being Fred, was so inspired at this romantic story and moreover, at the thought of him locating

and retrieving the steam fire engine that since

This beautifully restored horse-drawn Shand-Mason Steam Fire Pumping Engine would be typical of the old steam fire pump that allegedly had been dumped in the mill lodge.
©Alan McEwen Industrial Heritage Collection

hearing this tale, he had used a long iron rod to poke down through the quarry waste covering of the mill lodge every couple of square feet, in the hope of locating the steam fire engine. During the few days whilst working at Whitfield Mill, Fred was apparently experiencing wonderful dreams when asleep at home in Bolton, about rescuing the engine and taking it home to his yard and restoring it to its former glory with its brass and copper highly polished and the engine steaming merrily away. Alas, despite much poking into the soggy and smelly covering of the lodge, the steam fire engine, (if it actually existed) remained undiscovered.

As the chimney demolition preparation work was reaching its conclusion, Fred advised the demolition contractor for whom he was working for, to cover the windows of the empty offices with thick plywood sheets and to also protect the area of the mill lodge with a covering of old railway sleepers and iron plates. As he explained the proposed chimney drop to me, in his broad Boltonian accent, he expressed his concerns regarding the heavy stone chimney crashing down into the extremely narrow path between the offices, the cottage and the mill lodge; and should the chimney just veer over to the right and therefore land onto the unstable surface of the mill lodge, then the mix of deep mud and filthy water, perhaps several feet in depth and which was just topped with a few feet of quarry waste

WHITFIELD MILL, FACIT, NR. ROCHDALE

rubble, could be violently discharged on impact which would result in plastering the surrounding buildings with the mud.

I thoroughly enjoyed working with Fred at Whitfield Mill and I subsequently worked on one or two other chimney demolition sites wielding the rock-drill. During the large number of Fred's frequent chimney drops, usually executed on Sunday mornings I would regularly assist Fred, as indeed would several other friends and 'chimney enthusiasts' to stack the wood, lorry tyres and other combustible materials beneath the doomed chimney for the demolition bonfire. It became a sort of ritual and personally very exciting.

Sunday morning the 21st November 1990. The chimney has now been prepared for its demise and the lorry load of tyres have been tipped near the base which, together with wood, will form the fuel for the bonfire. Already numbers of people have turned up to witness the spectacular event ahead.
©Alan McEwen Industrial Heritage Collection

FRED DIBNAH'S CHIMNEY DROPS

Sunday morning, the 21st November 1990. It's extremely cold and overcast and there is a powerful wind blowing down the Whitworth Valley from the high snow-covered fells above. I arrived at Whitfield Mill at about 9 a.m. Fred and another old friend of mine, Neil Carney, who would subsequently become Fred's right-hand man, were hard at it, drilling air holes through the scores of pit-props that were holding up several hundred tons of the chimney. The whole set-up was to Fred's usual style: extremely neat and well ordered. A large crowd started to gather, all wishing to witness the death of this fine old mill stack, with perhaps one or two of these punters just hoping that something would go amiss. These characters seemed to get their kicks from looking on the black side of life.

As was my usual want, after bidding Fred "good luck", I then climbed up the western side of the valley to find an elevated location; a ledge where I then set up my cameras and tripods. From my vantage point high on the hillside, I could see the diminutive figure of my good friend Fred getting ready for lighting the fire which was carried out by a young lass at exactly 10 a.m. The police had moved back the large crowd to safe areas and I could still see Fred studying the rear of the 'gobbed out' chimney for signs of cracking. The fire was burning furiously, the chimney belching out massive plumes of pitch-black clag which was soon dispersed in the strengthening wind. A light drizzle and an overcast sky completed the scene; typically Pennine!

I really felt for Fred. For he often confided in me what it felt like when he was stood at the foot of a gigantic chimney with a raging demolition fire rapidly consuming the pit-props holding up the stack. His life, he explained, felt like, for just 20 - 30 minutes, out of control; it was his responsibility and his alone, to bring down the condemned chimney expertly as planned and devoutly safely! An exceedingly dangerous but profoundly expert job.

By 10.30 a.m. the smoke had almost ceased to issue from the chimney top and by looking through my field glasses, I noticed that most of the pit-props had burned away leaving nothing but fresh air supporting the exceedingly unstable structure which I could see was swaying to and fro in the strong wind. I felt really sorry for my friend, for I could imagine Fred would be sweating buckets and would be immensely anxious. He wouldn't, however show it to anyone.

With the demolition fire raging ferociously within the bowels of the chimney base, the scores of scrap tyres on the bonfire were producing voluminous plumes of pitch black clag.
©Alan McEwen Industrial Heritage Collection

WHITFIELD MILL, FACIT, NR. ROCHDALE

Always, the expert, professional, cool as a cucumber. I then heard the sound of the rock drill biting into the stone at the opposite side of the chimney from my elevated eerie. Suddenly, perhaps due to a sudden extraordinary strong gust of wind the chimney shuddered then lurched forward in a sort of slow motion; it broke its back in the usual fashion, and then with a tremendous roar smashed onto the hard cobbles of the mill yard. Hell's Teeth! Fred would have surely been at the bottom of the deadly unstable stack breaking out perhaps just a few stubborn inches of stone that were causing the chimney to remain standing. What a deadly job.

Due to the increasingly gloomy weather and with the light fading, I couldn't now see Fred. I was however, extremely concerned. I gathered up my cameras and tripods and dashed down the heather clad slopes of the valley side to enter the mill yard from the rear. A heavy pall of smoke and dust filled the air, making the crowd, who had now returned into the mill yard, to view the detritus of the demolished chimney, cough and rub their eyes. Anxiously looking around me for Fred, by now more than a little concerned for his safety, as the smoke cleared I was immensely relieved to find him surrounded by a large group of demolition contractors' men and well-wishers all heaping well earned congratulations onto our smiling and much relieved steeple-jacking hero.

The once dominant 160 feet tall mill chimney was now prostrated into a long, narrow carpet of crushed and smashed stones in an orderly, neat line running from the base of the chimney and extending perhaps for 300 feet. The troublesome mill lodge had thankfully been spared. There wasn't even one piece of stone littering the top. Just as Fred had planned, his Whitfield Mill chimney demolition had been carried out absolutely magnificently. The final move of the morning was to wash down the chimney dust with a pint or two of Daniel Thwaites's best bitter and all was well in the Whitworth Valley.

With the back cloth of a high barren Pennine hillside, the tall chimney topples to its death. All around the site is a hotch-potch of old mill buildings, engine houses, old terraced houses and more modern dwellings together with fascinated on-lookers.
©Alan McEwen Industrial Heritage Collection

McKechnie's Copper Smelting Works Chimney Drop, Widnes

Good Friday 29th March 1991

The famous local landmark at McKechnie's Copper Smelting Works, the 150 foot high chimney.
©Alan McEwen Industrial Heritage Collection

The early spring sunshine cast a welcoming golden glow to the tired industrial landscape of the copper smelting works yard. It was Good Friday, 30th March 1991 and accompanied by my young son Alasdair, we were standing at the base of a massive brick chimney that had previously received Fred Dibnah's expert gobbing out and pit-propping procedure in readiness for the gigantic bonfire, which was to be lit at 11 a.m.

I was chock full of nervous excitement for I enjoyed participating in, and witnessing the death, however sad, of these giant factory chimneys; I enjoyed also, the keyed-up atmosphere; the tension; that always preceded these dramatic chimney events. I liked the friendliness of the numerous 'chimney buffs' – who were generally middle aged men from near and distant parts of the country and who regularly and enthusiastically followed Fred's chimney demolitions wherever.

Fred Dibnah had spent the previous week 'gobbing out' the base of this monster stack and the affable steeplejack is seen here placing old lorry tyres in amongst the 'pit-props' that are supporting the chimney at the start of constructing the demolition bonfire.
©Alan McEwen Industrial Heritage Collection

A close-up study of the base of the chimney showing Fred Dibnah's expert installation of the supporting 'pit-props' and 'cap pieces'. Note also the large amount of brickwork that Fred and his assistants have removed from the 'gobbed out' area of the stack.
©Alan McEwen Industrial Heritage Collection

The author in the green boiler suit and flat tweedy cap is passing numerous tyres to other chimney buffs during the preparation of the bonfire.
©Alan McEwen Industrial Heritage Collection

This 150 feet high brick chimney was sited dangerously close to the factory buildings and also relatively close-by were a number of massive vertical, cylindrical steel oil and horizontal gas storage tanks, which formed a tank farm. All of these structures were within the drop zone of the condemned chimney that was going to be demolished by Fred that morning. By about 10.30 a.m. having received the nod from Fred and togged up in my old boiler suit and flat tweedy cap, with much gusto I commenced stacking mountainous heaps of scrap timber under the 'gobbed out' area of the chimney base, whilst ensuring there was plenty of the wood fuel placed between the props or 'sticks' as Fred called them. My son Alasdair joined in too, carrying small pieces of timber which he enthusiastically added to the rapidly growing bonfire stack. Other close friends, such as Neil Carney ,Fred's right-hand man, and fellow steeplejack Eddie Chattwood, Mike Bossan, Alan Brindle, a throng of chimney buffs and even members of the general public, which we regulars called 'the watchers' were also hard at it, lifting, gathering and stacking scrap baulks of timber, old wooden pallets, together with around forty large lorry tyres into the mountainous pile which formed

this sad old chimney's funeral pyre.

At precisely 10.50 a.m. when Fred was duly satisfied that we had built the bonfire to his complete satisfaction, he sung our collective praises by shouting over to us *"reet lads, you've all done a bloody good job"*. Our motley crew ceased operations and then dispersed to our pre-arranged locations around the factory yard to set up our still and video cameras. From my own chosen vantage point I could clearly see Fred, at his position at the chimney base, repeatedly look at his treasured silver pocket watch which was suspended from an attractive gold chain, and to note the few final minutes remaining prior to the bonfire being lit. Another minute or two ticked slowly by. Even though I had attended quite a goodly number of Fred's chimney demolition jobs, particularly at this point in the procedures I could feel the rapidly ascending thrill of excitement curse through me. I fully appreciated also, my mate Fred's most innermost thoughts, his anxiety; for despite the usual large and cheery smile on his face, and his jovial demeanour, I could sense Fred's extreme nervous tension, notwithstanding his obvious natural confidence in his own expert and professional abilities.

After the mountain of lorry tyres the chimney buffs stacked a large heap of demolition timber to cover them. Fred can be seen here preparing his bonfire lighting torch which consists of a long piece of wood with a diesel soaked rag fastened to one end.
©Alan McEwen Industrial Heritage Collection

Bang on at 11 a.m. and distant church bells sounded the hour. Fred could be seen in the front of the large bonfire handing a blazing torch made from a length of timber and diesel-soaked rag to a busty young lass clad in a bright top and tight blue jeans. Directed by Fred, the girl placed the burning torch into the two or three special pockets of highly combustible materials which had previously been inserted into the bonfire by Fred himself. Within seconds these 'glory holes' as Fred called them flashed into flame. Fred, taking the torch off the lass, then packed it into several other areas of the bonfire. Within two or three minutes, the whole bonfire material, having been previously soaked in diesel fuel flashed off. Within a few more seconds gigantic flames could be seen leaping up and great clouds of black, oily smoke could be seen issuing from the top of the tall chimney to pollute the factory yard and its surroundings. This smoke was so black and dense that now and again it even blotted out the sunshine and darkened the sky. Even though I was located over 100 yards away I could hear the violent roar of the high temperature flames being drawn up the insides of the chimney, and I could see that the diesel-soaked pit-props were burning

furiously. It wouldn't take long for this chimney to die. My watch registered 11.10 a.m. and the bonfire was still burning well, the lorry tyres producing enormous flames that were being sucked through the now considerably reduced timber pit-props shoring up the chimney and upwards into the throat of the stack itself.

Despite the smoke and mirk pervading the whole environment of the factory yard, I could still make out the diminutive and rather lonesome figure of Fred standing at the rear of the chimney base studying his horizontal crack detector, totally oblivious to the voluminous wreaths of black smoke and occasional large flames billowing from out of the bonfire. This simple device which basically consisted of a steel bar hammered dead level into the brickwork would start to descend once the strength of the pit-props had diminished due to the massive crushing weight of the chimney's masonry above, which in turn would induce a horizontal crack to appear at the rear. This is what Fred was actually searching for: evidence of the chimney structure starting to move. In Fred's own words, *"when t'chimney's feeling the t'pain"*. Meaning the strength of the pit-props had been considerably reduced and the chimney's ready for toppling.   Although from where I was placed, I couldn't actually see this crack detection device. I did however, then see Fred motion to a couple of the demolition contractor's men who stood several yards away from him, that the massive stack was about to fall. He then triumphantly sounded his air horn. From my location, the enormous bulk of the fire ravaged chimney suddenly appeared to topple over in slow motion, then within perhaps a split second or two, crack and break into three separate sections which crashed down with a phenomenally loud roar along Fred's pre-planned route, bang on target. This was followed by a massive dust storm which covered all and sundry which a mix of soot and ash.   Another fantastically exciting chimney demolition by master-steeplejack Fred Dibnah; and didn't he just win the spectators' appreciation all around. A loud cheer rang out and much hand-clapping. The once gigantic brick chimney was now nothing more than a long carpet of smashed brick rubble with a number of iron bands poking through.

The chimney's funeral pyre is now well alight, the flames moving rapidly in all directions. At this stage Fred is cheerfully requesting that the numerous onlookers move off to a much safer location.
©Alan McEwen Industrial Heritage Collection

With the fire burning merrily now, the lonesome figure of Fred stands to the rear of the chimney base keeping his watchful eye on the masonry where he has mounted his crack detector bar. Note the relatively near position of the railway line and the British Oxygen Company's storage tank farm.
©Alan McEwen Industrial Heritage Collection

The pit-props have burnt away and the 150 foot chimney commences
its descent to the factory yard.
©*Alan McEwen Industrial Heritage Collection*

FRED DIBNAH'S CHIMNEY DROPS

And down the chimney crashes in a massive cloud of dust, soot and ash. Another of Fred Dibnah's expertly engineered chimney drops.
©Alan McEwen Industrial Heritage Collection

Peering across the copper smelting works yard I saw Fred surrounded by the usual well-wishers and back-slappers, his face beaming with delight. There were also the usual autograph hunters, young children, teenagers, and even some

venerable members of the crowd bustling in around Fred eager to talk to him, compliment him, tell him what a star he was, and how much they had thoroughly enjoyed their Good Friday morning at Fred's chimney drop. There were also numbers of what some people would call rather strange men; these were the chimney buffs who attempted to emulate Fred's character by wearing flat tweedy caps, and they too would be complimenting their hero and would be asking him to autograph their most recent Fred Dibnah books and photographs.

Pushing through the crowd, on reaching Fred, and squeezing his right arm, he swung around towards me and with his already cheery face cracking into that wonderful bright and breezy smile of his, he welcomed me with his famous catchphrase *"did yer like that? It went really well did that cock. What a bloody belter"*.

As I have previously mentioned, prior to the lighting of the bonfire, I could sense Fred's tenseness despite his apparent carefree and jocular demeanour, for it was down to Fred to drop this chimney without causing damage to the surrounding property and plant or worse. For when there was just a handful of his closest friends within earshot, Fred would sometimes say

that he often felt a strange and weird mixture of fear and apprehension of the unknown, of the massive destruction that could be wrought if his chimney dropping did indeed go awry, coupled with the profound spirit soaring excitement, his professional pride in the job, the enormous passion, and also his appreciation of 'his' public following.

There was also a degree of sadness, for Fred would often wistfully say following the death of a chimney, *"there goes the end of another one";* his tone etched with emotion and perhaps the shedding of a tear or two. For Fred's world: the world that he knew as a boy in Bolton surrounded by his mills, his engine houses and his beloved forests of chimneys were rapidly coming to their end; for we were now living in the post industrial age and Fred Dibnah, despite being involved with the demolition process, due to his deep seated appreciation of Victorian values, Victorian engineering and craftsmanship, nevertheless, was often emotionally affected.

The author's young son, Alasdair, proudly stands in front of the smashed debris of the chimney holding the copper lightning conductor which originally had been fastened on the top of the stack.
©Alan McEwen Industrial Heritage Collection

The aftermath: a carpet of smashed and semi pulverised brickwork.
©Alan McEwen Industrial Heritage Collection

MONTON MILL CHIMNEY DROP, ECCLES, MANCHESTER

Sunday 4th August 1991

The tall and graceful Monton Mill chimney standing at the side of the Bridgewater Canal is reflected in the still waters.
©Alan McEwen Industrial Heritage Collection

Monton Mill, Eccles was built in 1905 beside the historic Bridgewater Canal and was one of the last cotton mills to be built in the Manchester area.

The Monton Mill complex had originally been reasonably extensive and a photograph taken in 1968 depicts a splendid long mill building of brick construction, five storeys tall, set at right angles on the western bank of the Bridgewater Canal. There was what appears to be a finely proportioned square mill tower of around eight storeys and more interestingly, another chimney significantly taller than the remaining stack that was to be demolished by Fred. Both the tower and the tall chimney together with the complete mill buildings had been previously demolished before Fred had won his contract.

I had only discovered that Fred Dibnah was scheduled to demolish the Monton Mill chimney on the Friday preceding the drop day of Sunday the 4th of August mainly due to me working away from my home base at Farling Top Boilerworks. However, on my arrival in Monton where I parked my car on some waste ground about a quarter of a mile from the mill site on the Sunday morning at ten o'clock, we were blessed with beautiful, warm sunshine and just a light breeze. Brilliant conditions for chimney felling work!

After parking my Trooper, I walked bedecked with cameras, tripods and all of the other apparatus the serious chimney buff requires, along the canal towpath. Being mid-summer the shrubs and trees bordering the canal were a delightful riot of colour. There were a number of gaily painted canal narrow boats moored alongside the cinder-covered surface of the canal towpath, and there were several boat-owners enthusiastically hard at work carrying out small, peaceful maintenance jobs such as painting and varnishing. As I walked past one particular attractive yellow-painted vessel, 'The Mariann', the delicious smell of frying bacon wafted over me to tantalise my nostrils and taste buds.

With the thought of a wonderful and tasty bacon butty in the forefront of my mind, on reaching the bottom of the graceful, circular brick chimney which I was pleased to see had retained its oversiller of moulded stone, I bade Fred and his mate Neil Carney a jolly good morning. Neil who was setting up the compressed airline from Fred's mobile diesel-driven compressor which was parked about 150 feet away gave me a friendly wave, whilst Fred greeted me with an enthusiastic and welcoming, *"Glad you could make it Al, I didn't think you'd come. They said you were working somewhere down south"*. "I'm happy to be here Fred", I cheerfully replied. Fred went on to tell me a little about how the whole of the Monton Mill complex had been demolished some time ago, which had just left the chimney standing all alone a few yards in from the canal towpath. Close to the bottom of the chimney I noticed that there was a large sign that proclaimed: FRED

DIBNAH HERE SUNDAY 4th AUGUST.

Fred and Neil had carried out the 'gobbing out' and 'pit-propping' procedures earlier in the week, and using some 'chimney buffs' to assist they had built up the demolition bonfire earlier that morning. I had therefore, nothing to assist my two friends with; my services were not required. "Isn't it an absolutely beautiful morning, not a cloud in the sky" said I breezily. Fred mumbled by way of a reply whilst chewing on a polo mint, *"Aye it's a bloody bonny day, just reet for the chimney drop, but I've got a reet drum-thumping headache. Too much pop last neet"*. He then filled me in with details of the mammoth bitter-drinking session that he and a very well known steam engineer and traction engine owner had endured until well after two a.m. that very morning. When he left Bolton to get to the mill site for seven a.m., he was fortunate that his trusted mate, and teatotaller, Neil Carney was prepared to drive the battered old Landrover towing the mobile compressor. As Fred stated, he was 'still three sheets int' wind' when he arrived at Monton Mill, and was still very much hung over. What he obviously needed was the 'hair of the dog', a pint of foaming Lancashire bitter! What could be a better tonic? But refreshments would have to wait until after the drop.

Fred's delicate constitution notwithstanding, within a short space of time subsequent to them arriving on site, he had fired up the compressor and using his air-hammer he had managed to chisel out several inches of brickwork from either side of the 'gob' in the chimney base. This work was followed as mentioned above by Fred, Neil and several other 'chimney buffs' constructing the bonfire under the 'gobbed out' section. The chimney was therefore, totally prepared for demolition.

I left Fred, who was, even though the day was still young surrounded with 'chimney buffs' and interested locals and I made my way back along the tow-path to a shady spot beneath an overhead canopy of cherry trees where I set up my two tripods and mounted my Olympus cameras. I considered this location with the Bridgewater Canal to my right hand side and the canal-bank trees and shrubs, particularly the overhead canopy of leaves very beautiful. Dead ahead was the Monton Mill chimney with its backdrop of modern houses that Fred called 'egg-boxes' – and they melded to make a rather splendid picture. The sun beamed down from an azure sky and the morning appeared to be getting hotter. I was extremely pleased. Life was bright and beautiful and I thoroughly enjoyed these chimney drops of Fred's.

My watch indicated it was 11.30 a.m., so with another half-hour to kill before the chimney's funeral pyre was lit, I made myself comfortable perched on an old five-gallon oil drum that I had discovered beneath the shrubbery. I got into a conversation with two bemused anglers, who were obviously amazed that somebody would want to photograph the demolition of 'just an old factory chimney' – as they put it. Unbelievably they had never heard of Fred Dibnah! I thought, Hells Teeth, what planet do they live on? Nevertheless, they were extremely pleasant young fellows. The anglers moved off in the direction of Worsley, and I was alone again. Glancing at my watch rather impatiently, the time was 11.57 a.m. By gum, just three minutes to go

before countdown. It was now really hot and beads of sweat running down from my forehead were making my eyes smart and I was being buzzed by a million blue-bottles.

Staring through my 200mm lens which was focused on the bonfire stack at the chimney base at a distance of around 200 yards, I could see Fred and another chap attempting to light the bonfire ignition torch. The usual problem of the torch not lighting easily, I mused. In a flash, I saw Fred hold up the torch, (a four feet length of wooden batten with a diesel-soaked rag wired on the end) and to thrust it into several different parts of the bonfire which immediately burst into flames. Within a few minutes the chimney's funeral pyre packed with tyres and diesel-oil soaked timber was blazing furiously and producing enormous, billowing clouds of dense black clag from the top.

With the chimney's funeral pyre blazing, volumes of thick, black smoke poured from out of the top. The lonesome figure of Fred can be seen standing at the base of the chimney.
©Alan McEwen Industrial Heritage Collection

The fire raged for around twenty minutes until the fire-ravaged 'pit-props' could hold up the massive weight of the towering chimney stack no longer. I couldn't see Fred, but I then heard his klaxon. Three sharp parps heralded the stricken Monton Mill chimney's imminent collapse; and over it toppled, breaking its back about a third of the way up the barrel. When it struck the mill yard there was an almighty thud and even though I stood some 200 yards away, I felt the tremor. A massive cloud of dense black smoke and brick dust engulfed the area of the chimney base and swirled around the nearby houses. A cheer rang out from the relatively small throng of 'chimney buffs' and onlookers. After packing up my camera gear, I walked across the rubbish-strewn mill yard to join Fred at the chimney base.

"By golly Fred, that was a brilliant drop, well done mate", said I. *"Yeah, cheers Al, but I got a reet rollicking off one of the Council Health Department's blokes about black smoke again. This guy showed me a letter, a copy of which was supposed to have been posted to my house in Bolton. Dear Mr. Dibnah... blah...blah...blah. we would request that you refrain from using motor lorry tyres when engaged in demolishing chimneys..blah...blah...... I'd already lit the bloody fire, when he thrust the letter into my hand, and he wanted us to pull out the wagon tyres, which were already blazing"*, said Fred in a most exasperated tone.

I casually asked him how he had dealt with the Council official. *"I just told him to bugger off"*, replied Fred grinning cheekily. He then went to join Neil who was loading their tools and airlines onto the back of the Landrover. A quarter of an hour after, I was with Fred, Neil and another close friend, Neil's daughter, Diane, enjoying a pint of bitter on the towpath alongside the canal barge that had been provided by the demolition contractor as a floating hospitality bar and was chock-full of beer, wine, spirits, pies and sandwiches for the Monton Mill chimney felling event's invited guests. I fully concurred with Fred when he said, "I had every confidence in that one, it were a belter. This pint o'bitter is just the ticket for my hangover".

The fire ravaged 'pit-props' suddenly collapsed and the 200 feet chimney falls.
©Alan McEwen Industrial Heritage Collection

Steam and smoke rises from the heaps of smashed brickwork and the crowd gather to take photographs. Fred can be seen talking to the hard-hatted representative from the demolition contractor's company.
©Alan McEwen Industrial Heritage Collection

Fred enjoying a pint of bitter and regaling the two ladies alongside the demolition company's 'hospitality barge'.
©Alan McEwen Industrial Heritage Collection

CONE WORKS CHIMNEY DROP, FARNWORTH, NEAR BOLTON.

Friday 18th October 1991

The Cone Works Chimney stands like a silent sentinel in the fire-ravaged surrounding mill yard.
Fred Dibnah with two chimney buffs discuss the proceedings.
©Alan McEwen Industrial Heritage Collection

FRED DIBNAH'S CHIMNEY DROPS

I had the pleasure of being personally invited to the Cone Works chimney demolition job, by Fred, who had called me on the 'phone at tea-time on the Monday preceding the proposed chimney dropping day which was to be the following Friday. To my mind the chimney drop to be done mid-week was contrary to Fred's usual working practice. This was because Fred was very superstitious about knocking down chimneys and other tall structures during the week, his long time preference being Sundays. Nevertheless, the demolition contractors who Fred was sub-contracted to, definitely required him to drop the chimney on Friday 18th October 1991 as the whole mill site had to be hurriedly cleared to make way for a new roadway.

A light drizzle fell from a leaden sky, as I left Farling Top at noon in one of the Boilerwork's Peugeot diesel pick-up trucks and en-route to Farnworth I picked up a close friend of mine, Ian O'Leary, an engineer and proprietor of a specialist steam valve repair firm in Keighley. Ian, like countless other folk, had watched Fred's steam engine and chimney-felling antics on the television, and had become an ardent admirer of my famous friend, Fred. He had, however, never actually met Fred, and therefore jumped at the chance of witnessing the Cone Works chimney drop and being introduced to the renowned Lancastrian Master Steeplejack.

By 1.15 p.m. the afternoon had turned colder with a chill wind blowing but thankfully the rain had abated and Ian and I arrived at Cone Works in Farnworth, a former small cotton and coalmining township, now a suburb of its larger neighbour, Bolton. Fred had previously informed me that the chimney demolition bonfire was going to be lit at 2.30 p.m. by his wife Sue. We had therefore, over an hour before the exciting event was to begin, and so we both trudged across the rubbish-strewn derelict mill site heading towards the chimney, which was a bonny, square-section 100 foot tall stack, built of Accrington red brick and looked to be in superb condition. The mill buildings, known as Cone Works and owned by a company called B.P.C. had suffered a massive fire resulting in severe structural damage.

A mammoth bulldozer was hard at work ruthlessly smashing down the fire-ravaged brick walls of the mill. Another huge machine was loading immense buckets full of brick rubble into a gigantic crushing plant. Demolition navvies could be seen tidying up all over the site. On reaching the chimney base we met up with Fred who was proudly sporting a large, bushy moustache and I quickly introduced Ian, who appeared a tad nervous.

"Oh you're Alan's mate, the expert at mendin' steam valves, are you? Hello, pleased to meet you mate. Could I cadge a bit o' valve grinding paste from you?" asked Fred, head on one side, his face a picture of friendliness and good cheer. Ian quickly confirmed that he would ensure that a tin of his best valve grinding paste would be despatched to Fred via myself. Fred was delighted. *"Coom on Al, I'll show you what we're about wi this reet, grand owd chimney"*. He gestured us to follow him around the chimney base to the 'gobbed-out' section at the foot of the stack. There was a small band of the regular chimney buffs stacking scrap timber and tyres into the void that Fred had cut out of the masonry. Fred's capable and efficient right-hand man, Neil Carney was directing the enthusiastic chimney buffs on where to place the wood on the bonfire.

"This little stack is a beautiful example of a well-built chimney, and in really good order. It's a shame you can't just lift them up and put them somewhere else", said Fred, whilst he was attempting to tie a diesel-soaked rag onto a stick to make his bonfire lighting device.

"I'm a bit concerned that the damned wood won't burn, it's been soaked through wi t'bloody rain", said Fred, addressing the small crowd of men standing around him.

At a quarter past two, Fred attempted to light the diesel soaked rag on the end of the stick without much success. The wind had dramatically increased and fine rain had re-commenced to fall. *"Bloody matches are wet through. Has anyone got a cig lighter?"* said an exasperated Fred. A couple of chaps stepped forward with cigarette lighters clicking away behind their cupped hands. Even then the rag, obviously very damp, refused to light. At this point one of Fred's helpers came to the rescue with small can of paraffin which he poured over the rag. Another session with the cig lighter and whoosh, the rag became a mass of flame. It was now the allotted time - 2.30 p.m.

Fred turned to his wife Sue who took the ignition torch from him, and on his command pushed it into one of the 'glory holes' within the bonfire. *"Reet cock, move over there where it's safer"*, he said to Sue pointing to a position well back from the chimney base.

With a chill wind blowing and a light rain falling an exasperated Fred seeks assistance in lighting the diesel-soaked rag on his ignition stick.
©Alan McEwen Industrial Heritage Collection

Fred expertly using his bonfire lighting device in one of his 'glory holes' in the stack of wood fuel.
©Alan McEwen Industrial Heritage Collection

Despite the rain soaked wood, with the usual few buckets of diesel being thrown onto the bonfire, the flames soon took hold. Fred cleared everybody except Neil from around the chimney and Ian and I moved over to a convenient vantage point behind a reduced section of the mill wall where I could set up my cameras.

We could clearly hear the flames singing and roaring inside the chimney. Coupled with the cacophony of exploding bricks, black smoke issued from the top and was carried by the strong wind across the town roofs. Within about 20 minutes, the raging fire had done its deadly work, the 'pit-props', by now, had been consumed by the flames, and we heard Fred's air horn sound the death-knell of the bonny wee chimney. The chimney suddenly appeared to life up from off its foundations and then majestically collapsed, breaking into several sections before crashing to the ground with a tremendous roar followed by an eye-stinging dust storm.

With just a few minutes left before its demise a long plume of black smoke issues from the chimney top.
©Alan McEwen Industrial Heritage Collection

The 'pit-props' have burnt away and the chimney is in the throes of falling to the ground.
©Alan McEwen Industrial Heritage Collection

The final act: the death of the Cone Works Chimney.
A brilliantly executed piece of chimney felling by the Master Chimney Toppler himself Fred Dibnah.
©Alan McEwen Industrial Heritage Collection

Due to it being a Friday, the admiring crowd was relatively small, nevertheless, a great cheer went up followed by Fred being surrounded with numbers of very happy 'chimney buffs'. Fred as usual completed his afternoon's performance with his famous phrase: *"Did yer like that?"*

After a few minutes of hand-pumping and back slapping, followed by the signing of autographs, Fred enthusiastically joined Ian and myself to enjoy a well-deserved pint or two of Guinness in a local pub.

RUGBY MILL CHIMNEY DROP CHADDERTON, OLDHAM.

Sunday 11th October 1992

Rugby Mill with the 180 feet tall brick chimney; in the mill block in the centre of the picture is Ram Mill, whilst to the left is the Byzantine style tower of Gorse Mill.
©Alan McEwen Industrial Heritage Collection

On a beautifully sunny Wednesday morning on the 7th of October 1992, I trundled into Rugby Mill yard in our firm's trusty 'Chariot' - an ex Royal Navy 7.5 tonne Bedford T.K. diesel, dropside lorry, to deliver Fred a present of a 25 foot long timber 'telegraph' pole. During a recent visit to my Boiler Works Fred had espied the 'telegraph' pole which was in fact an electricity line pole, lying in the Works yard, where the local electricity board had left it, following them replacing the pole with a much taller one and he had asked me if I would donate it for the forthcoming Rugby Mill chimney demolition job. My response was in the affirmative and I assured Fred that I would indeed be able to deliver the long, heavy pole to the chimney drop site in time for him to cut it into the 'pit-props' required to support the chimney prior to the demolition.

As I parked the Bedford Chariot close to the chimney base, I could see Fred, fellow steeplejack Eddie Chattwood and Fred's regular trusted assistant, Neil Carney fitting 'pit-props' under the 'gobbed out' section of the 180 feet high mill chimney.

Jumping out of my cab, I shouted a greeting, "hiya lads", and Fred and his two companions acknowledged my arrival with the usual "*hi Al*". I gazed up the tall red brick, cylindrical chimney and espied the name of the mill: RUGBY picked out in white glazed brickwork high up the barrel. There were a number of deep, long, jagged cracks in the brickwork. I then carefully made my way down the rather precipitous side of the excavated trench that had been gouged out of the ground around half the circumference of the chimney base, to join Fred and the other lads.

With the bulk of the Rugby Mill chimney rising up behind, Fred, Eddie Chattwood and Neil Carney
pose in front of Fred's trusty Landrover.
©Alan McEwen Industrial Heritage Collection

Fred, Neil and Eddie busily at work in the trench at the base of the chimney.
©Alan McEwen Industrial Heritage Collection

Fred expertly calculates movement in the Chimney structure following the 'gobbing out' process.

The view up the inside of the 180 foot chimney

©Alan McEwen Industrial Heritage Collection

"I see you've brought me the telegraph pole", said Fred, who still insisted on calling these long stout timber poles 'telegraph' or 'G.P.O.' poles, despite British Telecom being the main provider of his chimney dropping 'pit-props' material for a considerable number of years! I asked Fred why he had instructed the demolition contractor to excavate the wide, approximately five feet deep, semi-circular hole around the base of the chimney.

"This owd chimney, Alan, is unfortunately in reet bad health and will be a right bloody tricky 'un to knock down. Have you noticed the large cracks up on the chimney barrel?", said Fred. *"The thing is, not only is it cracked but the bricks are bad - right crumbly, and the whole chimney is only some five feet away from the side of the mill itself. It's as I said, reet tricky".*

He went on to explain that he'd had the large trench excavated because the ground floor level of the mill was approximately the same as the yard surface surrounding the chimney base, and his thoughts had been, that if they had actually carried out the 'gobbing out' of the chimney around three or four feet up, as per the usual procedure, when the 'pit-props' had burnt away, resulting in the fall of the chimney, the base could have 'kicked back' and severely damaged the mill building itself.

"So this is why we're working down here in't bottom of this here trench. It's like being on the Somme in the First World War. We've done the 'gobbing out' well below the ground level with the hope that when the stack collapses, it'll fall in the direction as I have planned, and not kick back." Clever stuff I thought.

Whilst I was down the trench, clutching my Olympus OMI SLR camera I slithered between the rows of Fred's expertly fitted pit-props until I emerged into the very bottom of the inside of the massive, tall chimney. Laying on my back and looking up, I could see a circle of bright blue sky and I fired off a few photographs. Shortly after, we all manhandled the electricity pole off the Bedford wagon and rolled it near to where Fred would later cut it into lengths to form more 'pit props' for the chimney.

I had previously done a little research of the history of Rugby Mill and discovered that the Rugby Mill Company had constructed the five storey Accrington brick Mill in 1908. By 1915, the spindleage totalled almost 114,000; the spinning mules were supplied by Platts of Oldham, and the whole mill was driven by a George Saxon 1200 horse power steam engine, powered by four Lancashire boilers.

Fred saws to length 'pit props' from the electricity pole delivered to site by the author whilst Neil and Eddie enthusiastically assist.

This study shows Fred in relaxed mood, about a half hour before the bonfire stack is completed, the waste wood boards and lengths of scrap timber lie to the front. Note, the steel hawsers wrapped around the stack and the corrugated sheet tin covering them over the 'gobbed out' section as a means of protection from the flames.
©Alan McEwen Industrial Heritage Collection

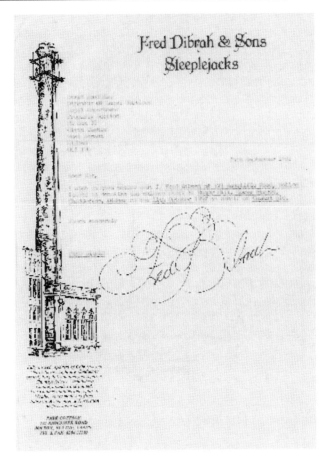

A copy of Fred's letter to his client Rugby Mill typed on his distinctive letterhead and signed in his beautiful Victorian copperplate.
Paul Donoghue Collection

(Top and centre) Cast iron makers plates from cotton-spinning and cotton-weaving machinery manufactured by Platts of Oldham.

(Bottom) George Saxon Ltd advertisement.
©Alan McEwen Industrial Heritage Collection

On a fine autumn morning on the following Sunday the 11th of October, I entered Rugby Mill yard again, only on foot this time. We had parked in a nearby street as vehicles were prohibited on this the morning of Fred's chimney drop from entering the mill premises. There were demolition men in yellow reflective jackets, donning safety helmets and a number of police to be seen wandering about the site. Scores of people were gathered in a large semi-circle around the chimney bottom.

I walked through a large crowd of 'Fred fans' until I reached the chimney base. I could plainly see that Fred, Eddie and Neil were down in the trench carrying out some final adjustments to the chimney dropping preparations. Fred and Eddie were drilling some large holes with an air-powered drill into the scores of 'pit-props' that I could see were supporting the enormous mass of towering brickwork above.   Neil was ably assisting by straightening out a mass of twisted compressed air hose pipes.

"Morning Fred. Morning Eddie and Neil. How's it going?" greeted I. My chums cheerily greeted me in return. I then noticed that they had wrapped some ¾ inch thick steel rope - 'hawsers' - several times around the chimney base which were covered with a galvanised corrugated tin sheet lashed into position. This was immediately above the area of the 'gobbed-out' section. Fred, on noticing me examining the wire lashings, explained in the fullest detail his procedure. *"The chimney's developed some fairly nasty cracks around the back, so the idea of fitting the wire 'hawsers' is a sort of attempt to try and keep the base together in one piece, once the chimney is falling so it doesn't break up and hit the mill wall. I've noticed from doing other felling jobs that if you get a stack with a load of big iron bands around the base that it helps to keep the chimney together as it falls over. The important thing is to keep as much of it, from shooting backwards, you know, by employing these iron 'hawsers' wrapped around t'base.   We've done these awkward, dangerous bloody chimneys before as you know Al, and our method definitely works. I know it might look a bit strange and a little on the puny side, but when you consider the massive, weight that we're dealing with - the trick is to keep the bloody thing contained sort of style", said Fred with a confident air. "If the chimney at the point of collapse has reached an angle of say forty five degrees, and the 'hawsers' have still got a firm grip of it, then it's not going to do any harm. It's not going to damage the mill wall when the chimney hits the deck".*

Pointing to the corrugated steel sheet which Neil had lashed to cover the wire 'hawser', he went on to explain: *"Them sheets of tin are there to protect the wire rope from the heat of the bumfire. Nevertheless the stack's so close to the mill, that it's an insurance man's nightmare. I'm full of confidence though, it'll be alreet".*

Fred's wife Sue, together with the Dibnah boys, Jack and Roger were close by, surrounded with friends, acquaintances and 'Fred fans'.

At 11 o'clock precisely, Sue and an attractive, young lady called Lorraine who had long brown hair were set to light the bonfire which was being hurriedly stacked into place between the pit-props down into the deep trench. I assisted this stacking of the bonfire materials in the time honoured fashion. Other friends, Mike Bossan, Alan Brindle, and Owd Jake all assisted Fred, Eddie and Neil with this heavy and dirty task. At the allotted time Fred motioned for Sue and her friend Lorraine to move nearer to the front of the chimney.

As usual there was a problem experienced in getting the torches to light. *"It's always a bit bloody embarrassing when you've got a time limit and you can't get the torch to light"*, said Fred wearily. *"This bumfire business, it always looks haphazard - but its my favourite way of bringing down a chimney and it always works. In the olden days of the Victorian era they always used coal for the bumfire, but you'd have to be a bloody millionaire these days for to purchase the wagon load of coal needed"*, he added.

The bonfire was lit by Sue and Lorraine and soon after, long flames were being sucked up into the maw of the 'gobbed out' section and up into the chimney's tall barrel. *"Two beautiful lasses - its gotta go right"*, said Fred excitedly. Plumes of inky black smoke poured out from the top and darkened the sky all across Chadderton.

"It's gonna be the last time this proud owd chimney blackens the skies of Oldham", said Fred pointing skywards to the huge pall of smoke. A few minutes later and Fred explained some more technicalities regarding his engineering of the demise of the Rugby Mill chimney. *"Due to us cutting into the base of the stack low down, the crack now induced by the weakening of the pit-props by fire, is actually somewhere deep below the surface of the ground, so I've just gone up the iron fire escape, which as you know is right behind the chimney and only a few feet away, to set up a stick which I've leaned against the chimney with a start angle of inclination of about eight inches. I bet that stick is now much straighter, which means that the chimney is actually moving in the planned direction of fall. I've tied a length of string weighted with lead to maintain the tension and when the chimney is really feeling the pain, ultimately the stick will fall out, which will mean the chimney is on the move and going to fall down. I'm going back up the fire escape now, 'cause I know things are going to happen within the next few minutes".*

"You're going to be very close to the stack Fred, and jammed between it and the mill wall", I stated, feeling rather concerned for my friend. *"It'll be awreet cock. It's sort of strange to be so close to such an enormous weight of bricks, which is going to depart right fast ... within a few seconds. It's a very unusual feeling, but I've jammed the door open on the fire escape, so I can shoot into the mill if owt were to go wrong"*, he assured me. *"There's no way I could have stayed down on the ground behind a big chimney like this one when it fell down. When I'm up on the fire escape, I'll actually be positioned just about eighteen inches off the thing - pretty frightening stuff, makes the adrenalin pump dunt it?".* He then raced up the cast iron stairs, whilst I hurried off to a safe position. From my location, I could just make out Fred's figure, high upon the fire escape landing stage between the now severely fire weakened chimney and the mill building.

Within seconds, three blasts were sounded on Fred's air horn, and the chimney majestically fell without breaking up - just as Fred had planned. Dust clouds and black choking smoke blew in wraiths all over the mill yard. A massive cheer went up from the general public and the 'Fred fans', followed by much clapping and whistling.
I met up with Fred at the base of the fire escape, and his happy smiling face said it all. *"Did yer like that? It were a bloody belter".* Everyone smiled and applauded him again. Lots of dirty-faced, excited children milled around, some holding up bricks which they wanted Fred to autograph.

The chimney topples and falls without breaking and exactly as Fred had planned the drop.
Paul Donoghue Collection

My 10 year old son Alasdair clutched such a brick, his young face beaming, my six year old daughter Shonagh at his side. Fred was clearly delighted for he really liked children.

Afterwards, he explained what it was like ensconced on the fire escape platform. *"I had a great feeling of confidence as I looked to the ground and saw the gap appearing in the cinder strewn floor between the chimney and the mill wall, and then I sort of just looked up to see the thing falling over, my eyes racing up the full length of the chimney barrel …. looking to see if it* were breaking up. *But it weren't however, it were just going down in one great, long bloody length. The thing is it were so good that I didn't have to run through the door into the mill. It were reet beautiful, Alan, there were no way it were going to get me. Eddie was located about thirty feet away down in the yard. I didn't need to be down there, I just stayed where I were on the fire escape landing. It never even scratched the window frames. That wire 'hawser' did the trick, it held the base brickwork until the very last second. I had every confidence in that one".*

A jubilant Fred strides out close to the heap of crushed bricks, whilst the mechanical excavator pecks at all that remains of the chimney base.
©Alan McEwen Industrial Heritage Collection

ATLAS NO. 4 MILL CHIMNEY DROP, CHORLEY OLD ROAD, BOLTON

Sunday 25th October 1992

Atlas Mill with its distinctive chimney. This image was taken two days before Fred demolished the stack.
©Alan McEwen Industrial Heritage Collection

FRED DIBNAH'S CHIMNEY DROPS

It was dinner time on the Thursday preceding the demolition of Atlas No. 4 Mill's chimney and Fred, Eddie Chattwood and I were ensconced on 'chairs' built from stacks of bricks, each tucking into a cardboard carton of rapidly cooling Southern Fried Chicken, which I had purchased a half hour earlier from the Asian-owned fried chicken shop on the corner of Chorley Old Road. All three of us were still quite wet from the continuous drizzle that had plagued us all morning. Nevertheless, Fred's job of carrying out the usual task of 'gobbing-out' the base of the 195 feet tall, octagonal brick chimney, the last remaining stack out of the original fourteen that had provided the draught for scores of Lancashire boilers on the extensive Atlas Mill's site, was going well. Ever since Fred, Eddie and Neil Carney had commenced work on the chimney the previous Monday morning, I had joined my three chums for a couple of hours each day, not to actually assist them with the prepping procedures, but simply to observe and take photographs which I thoroughly enjoyed.

I had been asking Fred all manner of questions relating to the history of the Atlas Mill complex, and with our dinner-break over with, Fred invited me to join him on a small 'recce' as he put it, of the partially demolished mill building.

The author captured this 'birds eye view' from the mill roof. Down on the ground at the base of the chimney are Fred and Eddie Chattwood and several other 'chimney buffs'.
©Alan McEwen Industrial Heritage Collection

121

Fred and Eddie chopping out some extra brickwork at the side of the 'gob'.
© Alan McEwen Industrial Heritage Collection

Fred led me into one of the impressive looking four storey mill blocks and then up a wide, stone staircase and out onto the top floor. The roof had been previously removed by the demolition contractors, which afforded us a most magnificent panoramic view of the Bolton townscape and mill yard below, a scene of 'bloody legalized destruction', as Fred stated, whilst pointing out numerous demolition men scattered over the enormous millscape with their mechanical excavators, cranes, gigantic lorries; all hard at work ruthlessly knocking down the old mill buildings. Being around ninety feet above the yard, we had a bird's eye view of the chimney barrel which was very close to the mill buildings.

"Alan, there was once 14 chimneys on this site and when I were just a kid, I used to come and look at some of 'em. I never thought I would be the guy to knock down any of 'em, especially the last 'un, the No. 4 looks so massive and indestructible", said Fred in a melancholy tone.

He went on in what I called his lecturing mode:

"This stack, Al, is next to the last of the biggest chimneys remaining in Bolton. It'll be very sad to see it fall, because I've sort of cared for it in one way or another since about 1965". He told me

that he had fastened his special name plaque made of mastic onto the chimney base with his impressed initials F.D., and that when he actually did it, he considered the chimney would surely outlast his lifetime. *"The chimney was built during the First World War in 1917, to replace two others when the war effort much depended on Lancashire's cotton spinning production. This 'ere Atlas No. 4 mill were built by John Musgrave and Sons of Bolton who were cotton spinners, cotton weavers and engineers in the period 1870 to 1880, and formed part of the gigantic Atlas Mill grouping that formed Atlas Mills numbers 1 to 8 and which dominated the Chorley Old Road and Mornington Road junction".*

Fred never failed to impress me with his deep and passionate knowledge of Bolton's industrial history. We walked around the debris-strewn carcase of Atlas No. 4 Mill, both of us, deep in thought, for we shared a deep passion for cotton spinning mills, and we were saddened to witness the death of this once proud structure; Fred particularly so. Fred unbottled his thoughts: *"These fine old mills really are what are referred to as the Dark Satanic Mills – bloody magnificent structures. You know, Alan, it'll be a very sad day on Sunday after I've dropped this 'ere chimney".*

Another panoramic view of Atlas Mill yard taken from the mill roof displaying signs of frenzied demolition activity with the contractor's cranes, heavy lorries and other machinery all hard at work reducing this extensive millscape into rubble. At the righthand side is the octagonal brick chimney shaft.
©Alan McEwen Industrial Heritage Collection

Fred perches precariously atop his mobile air compressor whilst engaged in filling the machine's fuel tank with diesel oil which he is pouring from a five gallon drum. Fred's Landover is parked, full of his specialised tools alongside. The all-dominating chimney and multi-storeyed mill block with its sightless windows rises to the rear of this image.
©Alan McEwen Industrial Heritage Collection

Fred chalks his centre-line on the brickwork base of the chimney as Eddie Chattwood looks on. This line assists Fred in determining the remaining strength of the chimney base brickwork when the bonfire has almost depleted the supporting 'pit-props'.
©Alan McEwen Industrial Heritage Collection

Whilst Fred and I had made our way around Atlas Mill, I took the opportunity of recording on film as much of the semi-demolished mill as possible. Shortly after, Fred went back to join Eddie who had recommenced with the chiselling out of the brickwork to form the 'gob'.

Sunday morning, the 25th of October 1992, the Atlas Mill chimney felling day dawned very cold with two inches of snow covering our yard at Farling Top. However, by the time I had driven the thirty-five miles over the Pennine Hills to Bolton, the snow had turned into heavy persistent stair-rod type rain and the sky a mass of dark, brooding clouds.

After parking my Isuzu Trooper in a nearby street and donning my boilersuit and tweedy cap, I entered the mill yard after informing the policeman on the gate, that I was one of Fred's team.

Fred, Eddie and Neil were hard at work drilling holes into the numerous 'pit-props' that now supported the massive mill chimney towering above the site. These 'pit-props' appeared to resemble giant's teeth. I greeted Fred and my other two chums, "Hiya Fred, hiya Ed, Neil, the weather's a bugger in't it?" Their clothes appeared to be sodden, the rain dripping off their caps.

Shortly after, together with other chimney felling regulars, all friends of Fred, Owd Jake, Alan Brindle, Paul Smith, Mike Bossan, we all got stuck into building the chimney's bonfire from a small mountain of scrap wood and discarded tyres that had been off-loaded to the front by one of the demolition contractor's enormous diesel dumpers. Within about twenty minutes, the team had constructed a massive funeral pyre and the scene was set for the destruction of the chimney. Whilst all of this work was being done, a large crowd had gathered all around, many togged-up in Sunday best despite the weather and prevailing mud and filth of the demolition site. As ever, at most of Fred's chimney drops there was a perceptible buzz in the air; a special brew of excitement, that I really liked.

FRED DIBNAH'S CHIMNEY DROPS

On the morning of the chimney drop with drizzle falling from a leaden sky above, Fred and Eddie drill holes through the timber 'pit-props', prior to constructing the bonfire.
©Alan McEwen Industrial Heritage Collection

Fred's wife Sue, lit the fire at one o'clock. and despite the rain-soaked wood, the fire soon caught hold, assisted by several buckets-full of diesel oil. As I watched from near the rear of the chimney base, my Olympus OM1 camera around my neck, I could see and was in ear-shot of Fred who was, as ever, peering through his glasses, searching for a horizontal crack in the chimney's basal brickwork to the rear of the 'gobbed-out' section, which would herald the collapse.

Black plumes of smoke poured out of the top of the chimney and the fire beneath violently raged; the sound of the white-hot flames being sucked high up into the throat of the stack could be plainly heard. It was making a hell of a roar. From my position, I suddenly heard Fred shout to Eddie who was alongside him, *"There's some large cracks racing up the barrel and accelerating reet, bloody fast. It shouldn't be long now. How long's t'fire been lit Ed?"* Eddie replied, "About twenty-five minutes Fred".

"Come on baby, you've been burning long enough", said Fred quite anxiously, *"it's time you bloody well performed"*. Suddenly, large cracks raced through the brickwork. *"It's time we buggered off lads, Eddie blow the sodding horn"*, bellowed Fred excitedly.

As we all quickly raced off to a safer position, we could hear loud and violent rumblings from within the stricken chimney. I shot a quick backwards glance, and saw that the tall stack was at last on the move. Then the beautiful octagonal, tall brick stack gracefully fell over before breaking its back at about thirty degrees of list. A tremendous noise like a clap of thunder was heard by everyone as the chimney crashed to the ground amidst voluminous clouds of smoke and dust. The rain-soaked crowd all together rent the air with a huge 'hurrah' followed by the usual whistling and hand clapping. Despite the chimney now lying shattered in a million pieces on the surface of the mill yard, the bonfire still burned brightly and clouds of oily smoke and steam rose up all around.

The fire has been lit and is rapidly consuming the timber and old lorry tyres that have been stacked under and against the 'gob'; wraiths of black smoke engulf the site and cover the rain sodden spectators with filthy, eye-smarting ash.
©*Alan McEwen Industrial Heritage Collection*

"What a grand send off", shouted a clearly relieved, yet immensely excited Fred, obviously very pleased with the outcome. *"I don't think we could have dropped the chimney any better!"* The crowd surged round their hero for the usual congratulations and the bestowing of bonhomies,

autograph hunters moved in with books and proffered pens, hoping to receive the famous Boltonian steeplejack's signature in his best Victorian copperplate, whilst hundreds of cameras recorded the event on film.

Whilst the rain increases, the chimney topples accompanied by loud applause and cheers from the watching rain-soaked crowd.
©Alan McEwen Industrial Heritage Collection

.... just micro-seconds from bursting into thousands of pieces the falling chimney with smoke still pouring from its top, plummets down onto the mill yard.
©Alan McEwen Industrial Heritage Collection

ATLAS NO. 4 MILL, BOLTON

A scene from Hades? The satisfied crowd clamber over the once proud chimney's remains whilst
smoke and steam rise from the mass of smashed brickwork.
©*Alan McEwen Industrial Heritage Collection*

Gathering up my family, we headed off as pre-arranged to Fred's Park Cottage on Radcliffe Road, where upon arrival, I joined up with Paul Smith and Alan Brindle in building a small bonfire in front of Fred's workshop.

Within a half hour there were several dozen friends of Fred and Sue's all enjoying the Atlas Mill chimney drop celebrations, jigging and dancing to the melodic and cheerful violin and guitar music enthusiastically provided by some of Sue's canal boating friends; the children all having a whale of a time, the adults with glasses of wine or beer. I joined Fred inside his Engine Shed each of us with an opened bottle of Guinness to hand. Fred exuding a paradoxical mixture of slight melancholy and intense upbeat

mood, quietly said, "*it's all very sad in a way really, Alan, 'cos that big, owd chimney that we dropped this afternoon went down really fine you know, like it landed in the reet shop, where we had planned it to go, but just like the story of me bloody life, I started my career wanting to preserve the things, but have ended up knocking 'em all down.*"

Later, during the celebrations I was introduced to Don Haworth the BBC television producer and his assistant Jean who produced the nationally acclaimed BBC documentary film 'Fred Dibnah, Steeplejack'

It was a pleasant ending to a most memorable day.

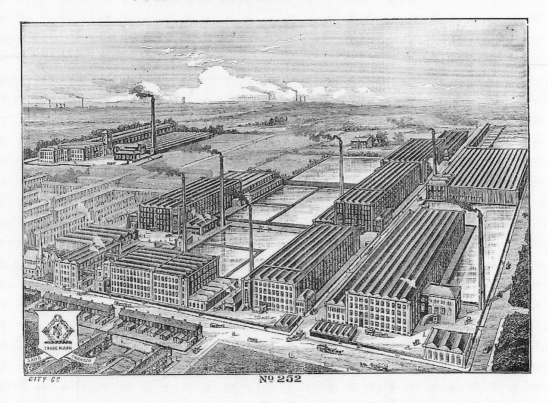

THE ATLAS MILLS, BOLTON, ENGLAND.

JOHN MUSGRAVE & SONS LTD.

Nº 252

FIG. 2.

Comprising six Spinning and one Weaving Mill, containing 362,000 spindles and 636 looms.

(Top) An engraving depicting the extensive Atlas Mills complex.
(Below Left) Pair of Tandem Compound Engine at Atlas No. 6 Mill.
(Below Right) Typical Lancashire Boiler

Reproduced from 1892 John Musgrave & Sons Ltd Catalogue
©Alan McEwen Industrial Heritage Collection

Pair of Tandem Compound Engines at Atlas Mill (No. 6), Bolton.

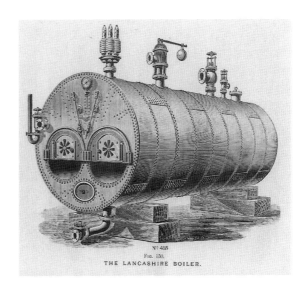

Nº 415
FIG. 150.
THE LANCASHIRE BOILER.

DERWENT MILL CHIMNEY DROP, COCKERMOUTH, CUMBRIA.

Saturday 7th November 1992

With the late autumn sunlight casting a mellow glow the 180 foot chimney rises above Derwent Mill.
©*Alan McEwen Industrial Heritage Collection*

FRED DIBNAH'S CHIMNEY DROPS

It was a freezing cold Saturday morning on the 8th of November 1992 and it was mighty unusual for Fred to demolish a chimney on a Saturday, but this coming Sunday was special: Remembrance Sunday, and Fred being Fred was an extremely superstitious chap. To drop a chimney on Remembrance Sunday therefore, was definitely out. Fred, Neil Carney and Eddie Chattwood, the Ramsbottom steeplejack, had worked most of the preceding week on the preparation for the dropping of this tall, octagonal and extremely graceful mill chimney which sported a massive square, moulded stone pedestal. The tall tapering chimney barrel was constructed from brick.

My family and I had motored up the A65 and M6 motorway to Cockermouth consequent to receiving Fred's typical cordial invitation to his Cumbrian chimney demolition project. On arrival on the mill site, I noticed that in a large area of the mill yard, for quite a considerable distance over to the left of the mill chimney's location, a large crowd of 'Fred fans' were gathering. There was apparently, a small admittance charge of about 50 pence each, the cash being destined to go to a suitable charity. At the front of the crowd, proudly strutting their stuff was the Biscuit Works silver band from Carlisle.

As I approached the foot of the chimney I quickly realised that the 'gobbed out' front and sides of the stone pedestal had suffered a serious fire; the pink sandstone masonry being blackened and a massive lump lay where it had fallen in front of the chimney base. Whilst I was excitedly engaged in firing off a number of photographs, Fred suddenly appeared, but didn't look his usual radiant friendly self. He looked tired, almost haggard. He greeted me with, *"Hiya Al. Look what some bloody minded sods have gone and done. Some buggars in the wee small hours of this morning had bloody crept in to the mill yard and lit the demolition bumfire that had been stacked under the chimney in readiness for the big event this afternoon".*

Fred wearily went on to relate how he and his mate, Neil Carney had been awakened early that morning at their lodgings by the police and fire brigade who requested that Fred attend the mill site most urgently, as vandals had lit the bonfire set beneath the demolition-prepared chimney, which had resulted in most of the 'pit-props' being burnt away. The 180 foot chimney was left evidently rocking to and fro in the light breeze. Fred was urged by the emergency service chiefs to make safe this deadly towering stack, post haste.

Fred and Eddie (as related to me by Fred himself), were pretty much still full of Cockermouth best bitter and Guinness as a result of spending the previous evening in a local ale-house, and were therefore, apparently not very tuned in for the exceedingly deadly work expected of them by the local fire brigade. Neil, however, was a dedicated tea-totaller, and although physically very tired readily volunteered to join Fred. Fred decided to leave Eddie safely tucked up in his bed to sleep it off.

On Fred and Neil's arrival on the mill's site they were met by the local fire chief who refused to allow any of his firemen anywhere near the mill chimney. It was therefore, the responsibility of Fred to ensure that the rather unstable 180 foot chimney was made safe. After walking over to the chimney base Fred and Neil got stuck into the profoundly deadly, dangerous work of clearing away the messy detritus of the partially-burnt bonfire materials, which was followed by the cutting and fixing into position of several new 'pit-props'.

Fred later recalled that despite the cold and drizzly weather, he had been thoroughly soaked through with sweat dripping from every pore due to the anxiety and stress he and Neil had to endure. Eventually, with the replacement 'pit-props' set into place and the chimney considered to be safe, they could both sigh with relief and Fred and Neil became the heroes of the Cumbrian police and fire service.

After complimenting Fred on his and Neil's obvious bravery I then left him and his two mates to get on with their work. I then climbed onto the flat-topped mill roof via several flights of internal stone stairs, with the aim of setting up my camera tripods in a location which conveniently over-looked the mill chimney. On looking over the stone slabbed parapet I could easily see Fred at the base of the massive stack diligently clearing away some compressed air pipelines in readiness for the lighting of the bonfire scheduled for 3 o'clock that afternoon. Because Fred had kindly invited my ten year old son Alasdair to actually light the demolition bonfire which had been stacked into the 'gobbed out' void at the base of the pedestal, I had scurried down the hundreds of stone steps clutching an Olympus OM1 camera which would enable me to record the event on film.

On Fred's command at 3 o'clock precisely, Alasdair lit the bonfire. Glancing over to the burgeoning crowd of 'Fred fans' and on-lookers who could view the proceedings at a safe

DERWENT MILL, COCKERMOUTH, CUMBRIA.

distance behind a temporary fence, I could also see and then hear the Biscuit Works band break into a lusty tune. Within a few minutes the fire had taken hold and was burning well. Ensuring that Alasdair was safe with my family and friends, I then charged breathlessly up the stone steps, three at a time, to emerge out onto the flat mill roof where I proceeded to take my photographs.

From my vantage point I could clearly hear a weird cacophony of sounds issuing from the tall chimney's innards which were sucking in voluminous quantities of orange-hued flames; black smoke pouring in great gouts from the chimney's cap. In spite of the smoke, the bird's eye view from my position on the roof was delightful and profoundly attractive; the small Cumbrian market town lying beyond the beautiful, silvery River Derwent, and with the majestic Lakeland mountains on the skyline.

The massive square section stone and brick pedestal 'gobbed out' ready for the dropping of the chimney together with the large stack of wooden pallets; fuel for the bonfire.
©Alan McEwen Industrial Heritage Collection

Fred enthusiastically instructing the author's 10 year old son Alasdair where to place the blazing torch used for lighting the demolition bonfire.
©Alan McEwen Industrial Heritage Collection

DERWENT MILLS, COCKERMOUTH, ENGLAND.

From an old postcard.
© Alan McEwen Industrial Heritage Collection

(Left) Derwent Mill, built in 1834 by Jonathon Harris and Sons was originally a flax spinning and weaving mill sited on the banks of the beautiful River Derwent that rises in Borrowdale in the nearby Lake District and flows through Cockermouth. Following the demolition of the chimney by Fred Dibnah in November 1992, the impressive mill buildings were converted to apartments.

The fire, well lit is rapidly consuming the large stack of wooden pallets. Fred can be seen cheerfully requesting the site dignitaries to move to a safer location.
©Alan McEwen Industrial Heritage Collection

Fred's expert calculations for the chimney drop allowed for the stack to fall and land on the concrete mill yard parallel to the river, and approximately a couple of hundred feet from the bank. However, due to the fire damage caused to the stone chimney pedestal by the vandals, fate would play its hand, and all would not go precisely to plan.

Still ensconced high on the mill roof and firing off shots with my Olympus cameras, I was suddenly joined by two well dressed gentlemen togged up in tweeds who introduced themselves as Directors of the company who owned Derwent Mill. Both were clearly immensely interested and were excitedly looking forward to Fred's chimney drop. The fire had been raging now for about twenty-five minutes. The tallest of the tweed-clad gentlemen, very politely asked me how long the chimney would remain standing. "Any minute now it should commence to fall", I replied with an

air of one who understood such proceedings. I then went on to relate to them both that I was proud to be a close friend of Fred Dibnah and had indeed attended numerous chimney demolition jobs all over northern England.

Another ten minutes slowly ticked by but there was no movement from the chimney, it was still standing upright. Looking over the parapet and down to the chimney base I could make out that the bonfire had by now burned itself out and there was very little smoke issuing from the chimney top. Instinctively, I knew that something was amiss. I could recall Fred's rather worried demeanour when he told me he didn't think there was enough scrap wood for the bonfire. So we had therefore, run out of fuel, I concluded.

The tall tweedy chap had obviously assumed that something was amiss. "Has the fire gone out?" he questioned, "and if the chimney doesn't fall

DERWENT MILL, COCKERMOUTH, CUMBRIA.

this afternoon" ...... (the late autumnal afternoon which had been sunny was now turning into evening and getting darker by the minute),...... "will Mr. Dibnah return and knock it down tomorrow?", the tweed-bedecked gentleman innocently asked. Well, despite my own negative thoughts, I obviously put him right by informing him that within the next few minutes the chimney would indeed topple. With a rising sense of foreboding I then once again looked down over the parapet and in the ever-increasing gloaming could make out the diminutive flat-capped figure of Fred carrying an air-hammer in one hand whilst hauling on a long length of trailing airline. Fred moved from the rear of the fire-ravaged chimney and commenced to gob-out some more of the stone and brickwork on the 'blind side' of the pedestal. This was the opposite side to where the large lump of stone had previously fallen off

following the act of vandalism. I then clearly heard Fred hammering away, the sound of the air-operated chisel cutting into the masonry could be clearly heard. What a dreadfully dangerous position for Fred to be in I thought; (I later learned that Eddie Chattwood was at his side with Neil quite close, too - all team members extremely brave men). The tall tweedy man questioned me yet again. He looked very concerned. "Fred won't leave my chimney will he and go back home to Bolton? Is there something wrong?" "No way, Fred will bring it down shortly", I blurted out somewhat exasperated. Then suddenly, there was movement in the tall, tapering stack. I propelled myself forward to look over the parapet. I noticed the brickwork at the base of the chimney had commenced to collapse. "It's going, going" I excitedly announced. I then fired off a sequence of shots with my Olympus cameras

The fire is burning wildly, the flames ravaging the 'pit-props' supporting the beautiful old chimney. In the background is the distinctive malthouse buildings belonging to Jennings' Brewery and the delightful Cumbrian town of Cockermouth on the other side of the River Derwent.
©Alan McEwen Industrial Heritage Collection

FRED DIBNAH'S CHIMNEY DROPS

A huge crowd of Cockermouth townsfolk and also two coachloads of 'chimney buffs' excitedly watch the awesome sight of the massive bonfire roaring up into the bowels of the chimney. Derwent Mill itself is to the right hand side. On the far left hand corner of the mill roof is where the author had set up his cameras.
©Alan McEwen Industrial Heritage Collection

The Derwent Mill chimney toppled gracefully and appeared to hang in the air for a second or two, and then crashed down with an enormous roar to land over to the right hand side of the projected drop-zone line, and a massive cloud of dust rose skywards. This all occurred in the blinking of an eye. I then heard a woman's voice half scream-half shout "FRED", and I looked over the parapet yet again. In the mirk down below at the chimney base Fred was nowhere to be seen. I was mortified with thoughts of my close friend Fred and also Neil and Eddie being pulped and buried under countless tons of brick and stonework. Still looking down, transfixed, the dust and mirk slightly easing, I then espied a solitary figure complete with oily flat cap emerge from behind the shattered remains of the chimney's pedestal. I then heard the distinctive Boltonian accented,

triumphant cry of *"did yer like that?"* Thank the Almighty, Fred was safe, notwithstanding being covered from head to toe in thick cloying dust, and I could see Neil and Eddie also were safe.

The huge crowd surged forward knocking down the fence and raced across the mill yard to surround and congratulate Fred. The end of an exciting but nail-biting chimney drop.

After the congratulations, and the taking of numerous photographs by the crowd, and whilst Fred was busy autographing books and photographs etc., Neil and Eddie were busy packing up all the tools and steeplejacking equipment onto Fred's Landover.

When Fred was satisfied, as pre-arranged, Fred

and his family, together with my family and close friends such as Neil and Francis Carney and Eddie Chattwood, drove the 80 odd miles down to our home at Farling Top, where we all enjoyed a grand old bash in the farmhouse after letting off fireworks at a huge bonfire I had previously built in the bottom fields.

As a consequence of Fred cutting out the last stubborn piece of brickwork, an exceedingly dangerous task, heroically carried out, the chimney commences to topple.
©Alan McEwen Industrial Heritage Collection

Another brilliant chimney drop executed by Fred, Neil and Eddie.
©Alan McEwen Industrial Heritage Collection

FRED DIBNAH'S CHIMNEY DROPS

The celebratory bonfire which the author had built at Farling Top with Fred, the Dibnah family and friends.
©Alan McEwen Industrial Heritage Collection

Fred said to the author "It's surprising that a few sticks of firewood, a bucket or two of diesel and a box of matches can create such ferocious splendour".
©Alan McEwen Industrial Heritage Collection

Whilst sitting around the bonfire enjoying a couple of bottles of Guinness, Fred blamed the bad luck regarding the chimney drop on a 'weird man' who had visited the pub in Cockermouth where Fred had been propping up the bar. Apparently, this individual was a salesman for a local firm of undertakers who had presented Fred with a pencil which had the name of the undertaking firm emblazoned in gold print on it. Fred seriously blamed the problems experienced with the chimney on this rather innocent gesture. He was an extremely superstitious character, was my friend Fred. God Bless him.

CAPE MILL CHIMNEY DROP, SHAW, NR. OLDHAM

Thursday 1st April 1993

Cape Mill chimney on the morning of the felling. Fred, together with his cohorts stand at the base.
To the left hand side is the stack of bonfire material. Note the boiler flue opening in the brickwork
in which Fred has placed two pit props for support.
Copyright Oldham Evening Chronicle

FRED DIBNAH'S CHIMNEY DROPS

Cape Mill was erected in 1899 by The Cape Spinning Company Limited and the company prospered. By 1915, the mill's spindleage was recorded as amounting to around 94,000; the spinning frames were manufactured by Platts of Oldham. There were four Lancashire boilers that provided steam for the mill's 1700 horsepower steam engine with the 200 foot cylindrical brick chimney providing the draught. Cotton production ceased in 1939 and the mill was subsequently used by Osram Ltd, for the manufacture of electric light bulbs until 1992.

In this ever-confident pose, Fred cheerfully gives the go-ahead for the lighting of the demolition bonfire.
Copyright Oldham Evening Chronicle

CAPE MILL, SHAW, NR. OLDHAM

Cape Mill's chimney designed by Stotts of Oldham, was the very last of the once numerous mill chimneys in the small cotton town of Shaw. Rising high as a backdrop to the rear of the mill was the dramatically dominating Pennine hills with their ubiquitous flocks of sheep and the dry stone walls that snaked up the steep fellsides to the heather-clad summits.

The preparation for the chimney felling took place over a period of three days prior to the actual demolition. Fred, Neil Carney and another regular chimney felling assistant, Ronnie, commenced with the cutting out of the chimney's base brickwork on the Monday morning, Fred's old mobile diesel compressor, which he had towed all the way from Bolton hitched to the rear of his Landrover, providing the compressed air required to power the pneumatic drills.

I had visited Cape Mill during this preparatory work to watch Fred and his two mates chiselling through the brickwork around the chimney base. Whilst Fred and Ronnie cut through the brickwork, which was discovered to be rotten, Neil would keep busy shoveling away the fallen brick debris and generally keeping the working area safe and tidy.

I watched fascinated as Fred and his men progressed at 'gobbing-out' and the fitting of the rows of 'pit-props' specifically cut to length on site, into the mouth which eventually extended either side of a vertical painted-on centre line, until around half of the chimney's circumference had been thus dealt with. These 'pit-props' were about thirty inches tall.

Walking across to where Fred was hacking out bricks at one hell of a rate, I tapped him on the shoulder and motioned for him to stop. Holding up a can of beer I shouted above the din being created by Ronnie around the other side of the chimney.

"Do you fancy a drop of beer, Fred?". With beads of sweat glistening on his forehead beneath the neb of his tweedy cap, Fred breathlessly replied, *"Aye, just the bloody job Al. I'm reet parched, it's this dust, it's everywhere"*. I passed Fred the can of coolish beer that I had just taken out of my Bedford TK lorry. I then stopped Ronnie to hand him a can of beer also, and because Neil didn't drink alcohol, I passed him a can of orange juice. All three men were clearly grateful for the respite.

After consuming over half of his can of beer in one long swig, Fred pointed to some new vertical and horizontal cracks that were running through the brickwork of the chimney base. *"The old lime mortar's knackered. It's only gravity holding the bloody thing up"*, exclaimed Fred, peering intently towards the cracks.

Fred went on to show me that there were seventy five bricks around the circumference of the chimney and from the centre-line of the 'gobbed-out' area he had painted several more white vertical lines and numbers. This evidently, was to enable the cutting out of the bricks to be carried out evenly and more importantly, to enable Fred to gauge as accurately as possible the moment when the several hundred tons weight of the towering stack had achieved what he had planned: that the load was taken up onto the 'pit-props'.

The day of the chimney felling was Thursday April Fool's Day and by lunchtime the weather was fine with not even a hint of wind. I had arrived at the Cape Mill site about two hours before the demolition bonfire was lit. Nevertheless, a large crowd of 'Fred fans' and interested onlookers were already there. I walked across the mill yard and around to the rear of the chimney, my boilersuit and tweedy cap underneath my arm. "Hiya Fred, a grand day for it". Fred was crouched down on his knees, peering through his spectacles at the brickwork. I could see his trusty set of trammel points had been set vertically into small diameter holes Fred had previously drilled in the brickwork about a yard apart. *"Hello Al, just look here"*, said Fred excitedly. *"The weight of the chimney has depressed the sticks by around three quarters of an inch, so by my reckoning the top of the chimney will now be some eight inches out of plumb, but the bloody bricks are reet loose and could give us a spot of bother"*. He showed me how loose the bricks actually were by tapping them with his hammer.

I noticed also that there was a long steel pinch bar hammered into a horizontal crack low down opposite to the 'gobbed-out' opening. This device was a well-proven method of detecting movement in the chimney, when the bonfire had weakened the supporting props. Shortly after, Fred jovially instructed us to commence with the building of the 'bumfire' – as he quaintly called the demolition bonfire stack. After enthusiastically donning my boilersuit and plonking my tweedy cap on my head, I lustily joined the small throng of 'chimney buffs', all regulars at Fred's drops, to stack the waste demolition timber and a dumper bucket load of lorry tyres around the 'pit-props'. When satisfied with our bonfire constructional efforts, Fred hurled several buckets of diesel oil onto the stacked wood and tyres. *"This'll make the bugger*

FRED DIBNAH'S CHIMNEY DROPS

burn", he said, as I watched the fuel oil thoroughly soaking the bonfire materials.

A BBC television crew had joined Fred at the chimney base and the camera men and sound recordists were hard at work making another fantastic Dibnah Chimney Drop film. Fred appeared as ever, totally confident and humourous. However, there appeared to be a spot of bother concerning the lighting of the bonfire ignition torch, which was quite usual and almost considered by now to be part of the ceremony.

Fred appeared a trifle embarrassed when the man attempting to light the torch, who had won a competition in the local newspaper to become Fred's invited guest, had gone through half a box of matches. Fred quipped, *"There's always a bit of trouble with the ignition system, especially since I packed in smoking!"* A minute later, the deed was done and the torch was merrily blazing away. Fred instructed the man to place the torch into the bonfire which caught fire spontaneously.

Within a couple of minutes, due to the oil-soaked mill floorboards that we had used to build the bonfire, there were masses of pitch-black smoke tinged with orange pouring out of the chimney top. The scores of old lorry tyres erupted into flames and the black smoke became even more dense. There was a strong smell of burning rubber that got up your nose and made your eyes water. The noise of exploding bricks inside the chimney and the roar of the angry fire filled the air. I was stood just a few yards away from where Fred was crouched at the rear of the chimney base watching for movement in the steel pinch bar.

Looking over to where I stood, he smiled and pointed to the inky black cloud of smoke that was rapidly darkening the pale blue sky above Shaw. *"It's like the ceremonial burning of a witch"*, he cheerfully quipped. The television crew homed into every conceivable move Fred made. The cameramen, sound engineers and director clearly enjoyed the mounting drama. This was, after all, damn good television.

The stricken chimney stands with a back-cloth of rooftops and the Pennine hills beyond; the fire rages furiously and smoke and fumes pour from its top and a deluge of bricks can be seen falling down.
Copyright Oldham Evening Chronicle

CAPE MILL, SHAW, NR. OLDHAM

Glancing at my watch, I reckoned that the bonfire had by now been burning for over five minutes. Shooting a quick glance over to Fred, I saw him suddenly jump up and move several yards further back from the chimney base. Whilst shouting *"It's gawing, gawing",* he operated his klaxon to produce four blasts. Looking up to the chimney top, I saw it suddenly shudder and there was the unmistakable sound and sight of a heavy load of bricks falling down both inside and outside the

barrel; the stricken chimney then toppled over and majestically fell in what appeared to be slow motion and landed spot on the drop zone. Clouds of dust filled the air and covered Fred and the small handful of brave souls who had remained just a few yards to the rear of the chimney. A tremendous gasp followed by cheers and whistles filled the air. The large crowd went wild and rushed over to encircle Fred; the hero of the hour.

A dramatic image: with smoke issuing from its top the Cape Mill chimney commences to topple ....

.... and crashes to the ground in a cloud of smoke and dust.

Copyright Oldham Evening Chronicle

"Fred over here, Fred mate", shouted a newspaper cameraman. "Mr. Dibnah, will you please autograph my book for my young grandson?", requested a grey-haired elderly lady who thrusted a copy of 'FRED DIBNAH – STEEPLEJACK' towards the sooty figure of Fred.

From the lighting of the bonfire, the destruction of the ninety-four year old brick mill chimney had taken just nine minutes.

"It's over, done for. I actually expected it to disintegrate due to the lack of mortar in the brickwork but it went spot on just where I wanted it to go. There were a few bricks flying around my head. A bit hairy like. Never mind Alan, it were a beauty and even though I feel reet sad that I've dropped another chimney, I am very pleased that the job's gone well to plan, particularly with it

being April Fools' Day. Now it's down there's just a big space in the sky", exclaimed Fred with a relieved look on his face.

Later, he told me that just prior to the fall of the stack, that he noticed the chimney barrel had a significant number of large cracks running vertically, that continued cracking higher and higher, until the chimney finally toppled over.

We then left Cape Mill yard to walk a short distance to a nearby pub to slake our thirst and to celebrate another of Fred Dibnah's chimney dropping triumphs.

OWL MILL CHIMNEY DROP
LEES, NEAR OLDHAM

18th July 1993

Owl Mill, Lees on the morning of Fred Dibnah's chimney drop. Children, teenagers and old men stand watching the awesome sight of the demolition men's crane with its giant iron ball reducing this once proud mill to rubble. The Stott designed chimney rises starkly in the background against the sky.
©Alan McEwen Industrial Heritage Collection

When I was phoned by Fred to tell me about this particular chimney drop and to invite me to attend, I then recalled Owl Mill, for back in the 1960s I had actually done a minor riveting job on one of the Lancashire boilers that had originally provided the steam for the mill engine. I was, therefore, extremely interested and had great pleasure telling him that wild horses would not stop me from going.

After driving down the Pennine 'spine' through a number of interesting former woollen and cotton towns: Burnley, Todmorden, Littleborough, Milnrow, and Shaw, all of which still had surviving textile mills and chimneys, although some had been sadly decapitated, we drove through Oldham's strangely named suburb, Mumps Bridge, then after about another three miles of driving uphill towards the Pennine watershed and the West Yorkshire border, we arrived in the pleasantly located hill village of Lees at 9.45 a.m. The impressive structure of Owl Mill could be seen away on the left, towering high above a short row of terraced dwellings.

It was a beautifully sunny morning and I parked my car on the edge of the mill yard. Looking across to the truncated chimney constructed from brick to the design of Oldham architects, Stott and Co., I could see Fred filling the diesel tank on his mobile air compressor. Collecting my Olympus cameras after donning a boiler suit, my steel toe-capped boots and plonking my tweedy cap on my head, I sauntered over to Fred, who, having his back to me, had not seen me approach. "Morning Fred, what a grand old mill. It's a tragedy that its getting the big hammer". He swung around quickly and in doing so splashed quite a large amount of red diesel all over the compressor engine. *"Whoops, bloody hell. Dun't it stink this damn stuff? How're you doin' Al? Welcome to Owl Mill".*

I asked him if he needed any assistance in building the bonfire beneath the 'gobbed out' chimney base which I could plainly see. *"Aye, when you're reet, join in wi t'other lads, Mike and Neil are around somewhere"* Fred said. "I'm going to fire off a few pictures first of all and have a good look around. I'll see you in about twenty minutes", I replied.

The demolition contractors were employing a massive crawler crane to which was attached an enormous iron ball to batter down the brickwork of the multi-storeyed mill buildings. The crane driver expertly swung the ball which must have weighed, I guessed, about 2 tons with much gusto at the tall brick wall. Every strike of the ball brought down an avalanche of smashed brick which was building up into huge piles.

Choosing a relatively peaceful and hopefully safe area to set up my camera tripod amidst a small jungle of Buddlea shrubs which were covered in dazzling beautiful butterflies, I thought how wonderful nature was to recapture what man and industry had in earlier times despoiled. There were some lovely wild flowers growing in the cinder-covered yard, yellow headed dandelions, purple rose bay willow herb and thousands of large white daisies. What a delight! Old industrial sites could often become veritable nature reserves within just a short time. Looking across the main road, I saw another splendid looking mill with a tall, brick chimney which sported the mill's name 'LEES BROOK' picked out in white bricks high on the barrel. That mill looked like it was still working: still providing employment for local people.

At the chimney base Fred's helpers are eagerly stacking scrap timber joists whilst constructing the demolition bonfire. Fred's compressor is to the left of the men whilst in the background is the tall slender stack of Lees Brook Mill.
©Alan McEwen Industrial Heritage Collection

FRED DIBNAH'S CHIMNEY DROPS

I fired off a couple of photographs of Owl Mill and I felt very saddened to see the once fine mill architecture now in its death throes. I heard a man's voice. Looking behind me, I saw an elderly man with white hair standing on a flagstone path just beyond the clump of Buddlea bushes. "Hello, hello young man. Can I come in and watch t'mill chimney stack be dropped?" He asked. "Mornin' mate, I'm sure it will be alright, but I'll ask Fred Dibnah for you". "That's very decent of you, lad", the old man replied. I informed him that he could walk over to the chimney bottom with me in a few minutes. Meanwhile, I went over to join him and got chatting. The old man, I'll call him Mr. Jones, was over 80 and had worked at Owl Mill for many years as the 'fire beater', stoking the two Lancashire boilers. He started to relate to me some of the history of Owl Mill.

"Owl Mill was built in 1898 and was driven by a large 1500 horse power steam engine built in Bolton by John and Edward Wood. All of the spinning frames were made and fitted by Platt Bros. of Oldham". He went on to say that during the First World War, Owl Mill operated over 100,000 spindles. Bad times befell Owl Mill resulting in closure in 1956. However, it re-opened in 1964 following massive rebuilding and the installation of new machinery. The mill finally closed down in 1990. The old stoker said it was a very sad day for Owl Mill and for Lees.

We both walked over to the chimney where I met up with another fellow chimney buff and traction engine driver, Mike Bossan. I found Fred and introduced the old fire beater. Fred made the old man most welcome and ending up having a lengthy animated discussion about stoking coal onto Lancashire boilers using No. 14 coke shovels! Fred then autographed a cigarette packet for him. Old Mr. Jones was clearly delighted.

The expertly 'gobbed out' and 'pit-propped' chimney base with Fred and one of his assistants drilling holes into the timber 'pit-props'. This procedure assists the fire to reduce and destroy the 'pit-props' more expediently. Fred's 'workhorse' his trusty Land Rover is in the background.
©Alan McEwen Industrial Heritage Collection

FRED DIBNAH'S CHIMNEY DROPS

After lending a hand to Mike, Neil and a few of the other regular 'chimney buffs' with the construction of the bonfire, by 11.20 a.m. it was ready for lighting. A few minutes ticked by. I always found this stage of the event extremely exciting. Fred and another chap walked up to the bonfire, each carrying a bucket of diesel fuel oil, which they hurled over the scrap timber and tyres.

It was by now 11.30 a.m. The allotted time. A young woman then stepped forward out of the large crowd of Lees' villagers and sundry onlookers, *"Hiya cock",* said Fred sporting a beaming smile. *"Here, take this torch and when I give you the word, stuff it int' firewood".* Fred tendered the burning torch, which was a four feet length of 2" x 1" wood with a diesel-soaked rag wired to one end merrily blazing away, to the lass. *"Reet, stick it in theer, love",* Fred said, pointing to 'the glory hole' beneath the bonfire. *"Reet love, its burning. You can move back towards the crowd now. Thanks love",* he added, flashing the lass a pleasant smile.

Within minutes of the fire being started, enormous oily flames were being sucked into the chimney's insides, which made a loud roaring sound. By now, the police had moved all of the crowd to a safe area at the other end of the mill yard. I then re-joined my family who were standing at the far side of the mill yard on a slightly elevated area. Just right for me and my trusty camera.

The fire is well alight and the flames are being sucked into the bowels of the chimney. On the right Fred can be seen directing some of his invited guests where to safely watch.
©Alan McEwen Industrial Heritage Collection

FRED DIBNAH'S CHIMNEY DROPS

The fire burned so fiercely, no doubt due to the oil-soaked timber and the numerous tyres that we had packed around the 'pit-props', that within less than 25 minutes, I heard Fred shout *"its gawing, gawing"*. Quickly followed by the sound of his horn. I then saw the 140 foot brick stack with Owl Mill, the name of the mill emblazoned in white brick high up on the chimney commence to topple and then quickly collapse.

Volumes of ink-black smoke, and the inevitable dust storm blanketed the site. People were coughing. I had a speck of dust in my left eye causing my eye to leak. (Not a tear, honest). Never mind. What a bloody, brilliant chimney drop. Well done Fred, Old Pal.

A massive pall of thick black smoke rises from the condemned chimney top. The fire rages at the base with the massive bulk of the semi-dismantled mill structure at the rear.
©Alan McEwen Industrial Heritage Collection

"It's gawing, gawing", shouts Fred. The fire has done its work and the pit-props have now burned
away causing the chimney to lean over and collapse.
©Alan McEwen Industrial Heritage Collection

**The rapidly disintegrating chimney shudders into an enormous heap of brick rubble. The end of
another one!**
©Alan McEwen Industrial Heritage Collection

N. GREENING & SONS LIMITED CHIMNEY DROP, BRITANNIA WIREWORKS, WARRINGTON.

Sunday 17th April 1994

Greenings 150 foot stack on the morning of the demolition.
Peter Foy Collection

The venue for this particularly splendid and most successful chimney drop carried out by Fred was the historically interesting and extensive wireworks that covered some twenty-seven acres on Bewsey Road.

Nathaniel Greening was born in the small village of Cambridge near Dursley, Gloucestershire on the 12th of April 1780. He established his famous wireworking business on Bridge Street in the centre of Warrington in 1799. Greening was a clever man, an early pioneer who was fascinated with wireworking, and who carried out numerous successful experiments on steam powered looms similar to types used in textile mills, to produce woven wire mesh. Several of Greening's early business associates such as the Ryland brothers

and Thomas Locker were also entrepreneurs in Warrington's burgeoning wireworking industry and set up factories of their own, which resulted in the Lancashire town eventually becoming world famous for wire manufactured products. In 1807 wire-drawing was carried out at the Bridge Foundry and later at a mill located at the top of Church Street in the town. It was during this period that Nathanial Greening invented the first successful steam-powered looms specifically for wireworking.

In July 1843 Nathaniel Greening was joined in the business by his three sons, Timothy, Noah and John. In December 1853, Timothy left the firm, leaving the ownership of the rapidly-flourishing business to his two brothers Noah and John.

N. GREENING & SONS LIMITED, WARRINGTON

In 1883, the firm was managed by the grandsons of the founder (who had died in 1860) – Nathaniel and Linnaeus Greening, and in the same year a new limited liability company was formed: N. Greening and Sons Ltd; who promoted themselves as being 'wire manufacturers, wire workers, brush manufacturers, metal perforators and engineers'. The firm would eventually become renowned for manufacturing wire mesh, metal conveyor belts for the mining and extractive industries, special wire mesh filters in ferrous and non-ferrous metals and also for production of wire and rods for nail-making, bolt and rivet manufacture.

Around 1900 the firm moved to a large twenty seven acre site on Bewsey Road, which originally was a brick-field and the new construction of the Britannia Works began. Navvies engaged on digging foundations for the works discovered an abundance of quality clay, which the firm used for the making of thousands of bricks. Between 1905-1906 the whole of Greening's company moved from the old works to the new Britannia Works on the Bewsey Road site.

Following the Second World War, Greening's Britannia Wireworks employed over one thousand personnel. The heating and manufacturing process steam requirement was provided by two Lancashire boilers. The 150 foot tall, circular brick chimney built in 1900 was used to provide draught for the boilers and to carry away the smoke. The bricks used in the construction were manufactured from Bewsey clay originating from the Works site. Sadly this fine looking chimney became redundant in 1984. There was also a large Browett and Lindley reciprocating horizontal steam engine built in nearby Patricroft, which generated electricity for the works.

During Fred's chimney drop I actually saw this steam engine, whilst exploring these fascinating works, most of which were being demolished at this period.

A close-up of the chimney showing the supporting 'pit-props'. Fred's diesel compressor and the huge stack of bonfire material is in the foreground.
Peter Foy Collection

Fred hurls a bucket of diesel oil onto the stacked bonfire materials.
Stan Davies Collection

Fred's Chimney Drop:

On my arrival on the site and walking over to the chimney I could see that Fred had completed all of the necessary chimney demolition procedures, leaving just the bonfire to be constructed beneath the large number of 'pit-props' that were supporting the 150 feet tall stack.

Looking around the site for Fred who was not at the chimney base, glancing over to a rake of long open-sided sheds I saw him engaged in animated conversation with a number of pin-stripe suited,

important looking types, whom I later learnt were some of Greening's dignitaries. Nevertheless, after catching his eye, he waved a typical friendly greeting over to me.

At about 11.45 a.m. we, the usual gathering of 'chimney buffs', commenced stacking the pieces of broken old timber, much of which had been ripped out of the surrounding semi-derelict works buildings, old lorry tyres and a massive pile of semi-rotten linoleum to form the chimney's funeral pyre.

Fred shows an invited audience of young children including my son Alasdair and Fred's son Jack, the intricacies of the bonfire stack.
©Alan McEwen Industrial Heritage Collection

By 11.55 a.m. a large crowd had gathered, many being Greening's employees, together with their families. At 11.58 a.m. Fred was ready to commence the ceremony of lighting the bonfire ignition torch, a yard long length of roofing lathe with rags multi-wrapped around one end, the whole soaked in diesel fuel oil. The deed was done and the ignition torch burst into flame.

Moving forward Fred handed the torch to a young woman wearing an orange safety helmet who came from within the crowd of onlookers, and instructed her where to thrust it into the gigantic pile of combustible material stacked in and around the 'gobbed-out' section of the chimney base. Within a couple of minutes, the bonfire was blazing fiercely. Smoke in great dense black clouds issued out of the chimney's top and was blown with the light breeze across the nearby railway line.

Fred moves forward with his blazing ignition torch to light the bonfire, whilst gathered around are several 'chimney buffs' and fascinated children.
Stan Davies Collection

A dramatic shot of the bonfire fiercely burning with massive orange-hued flames leaping into the air. Fred can be seen nonchalantly staring at the massive clouds of thick, black smoke, whilst a video cameraman records the scene. The green boiler-suited, tweedy-capped individual scurrying away is the author, who is running over to where he will be able to safely photograph the unfolding dramatic event .
Stan Davies Collection

I found a position to set up my Olympus camera tripod away from the crowd, but I could still see Fred who was pacing about at the rear of the chimney base studying his steel pinch-bar which had been driven into a horizontal mortar joint low down, for signs of movement. You could easily hear the roaring noise that the flames made as they were sucked through the ever-weakening 'pit-props' and up into the throat of the chimney.

After about twenty minutes of inactivity, I could discern a murmur coming from the crowd of onlookers. Looking across to where Fred was crouched onto the ground at the back of the stack, I saw him rise to his feet holding his trusty klaxon horn in his right hand. He scurried away further behind the chimney. Within about a half a minute more, I saw Fred stoop to the klaxon, then I heard the distinctive sound of it reverberate all around the wireworks yard. *"It's gawing, gawing"*, shouted an excited Fred. Then the tall chimney moved as the 'pit-props' buckled under the weight and it collapsed hitting the hard concrete of the yard with a loud thump. "Hurray, hurray", shouted the gleeful crowd followed by the usual whistling and clapping of hands.

Moving over to Fred I congratulated him. *"It were a good un. Everything went according to plan"*, he said, his face a smiling picture. I later spoke with an employee, who had worked on the wireworks site for 46 years, "It's the end of an era, there won't be another wireworks like Greenings of Warrington", the man said emotionally.

The chimney collapses, the barrel breaking in two.
Stan Davies Collection

(Left) Advertisement for Browett, Lindley & Co. Ltd. High-speed steam engines.
(Right) Makers plate from a Browett, Lindley steam driven electrical generating plant.
(Both) ©Alan McEwen Industrial Heritage Collection

The lone figure of Fred can be seen at the rear of the chimney watching its final death throes.

As a dramatic dust cloud rises; Fred remains in the same position.

Sue Gould Collection

The End.   Men, women and children clamber over the large mound of smoking rubble, many of them clutching a hot brick in their hands for Fred to autograph.

©Alan McEwen Industrial Heritage Collection

Greening and Sons advertisement taken from a trade catalogue dated 1871.
©Alan McEwen Industrial Heritage Collection

The extensive Britannia Works situated alongside the London to Glasgow railway line
photographed in 1949. (Warrington & District Trade Catalogue 1950).
©Alan McEwen Industrial Heritage Collection

ASIA MILL CHIMNEY DROP, CARTER STREET, GREAT LEVER, BOLTON

Monday 23rd November 1998

Asia Mill with the demolition contractor's six-wheeled, ERF skip wagon, next to which is a Bobcat loading shovel.
Mick Berrry Collection

The 160 feet high brick chimney belonging to the Asia Mill was one of the last tall mill chimneys in Bolton to be demolished by Fred.

Asia Mill was a huge five storeyed brick cotton spinning mill built in 1895 for Wolfenden & Son Ltd, members of the massive Fine Spinners and Doublers Association Limited.

This architecturally striking Bolton mill closed around 1995 and by 1998 the demolition process went into full swing as the land was required for the construction of new premises for a local office equipment company.

157

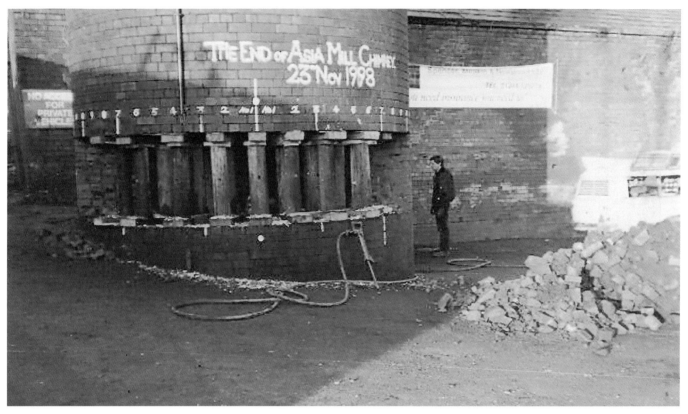

The chimney base displaying the neatly engineered 'gob' and the 'pit-prop' supports; note also, the poignantly worded slogan: THE END OF ASIA MILL CHIMNEY 23RD NOV 1998.
Mick Berry Collection

This was another of Fred's chimney drops that, despite him inviting me, I didn't attend due to other commitments and I was very saddened that I missed the drama and excitement of the demise of the Asia Mill chimney. Nevertheless, a few days following the event, on visiting Fred, it didn't need much badgering to get him to dramatically relate to me the details of the Asia Mill Chimney drop.

Fred's Story:

"Me and my old mate Mick Berry tackled this here chimney, which even though the top had been removed many years earlier, it were still quite a big cotton mill chimney of some 160 feet in height. We found the bricks at the base to be pretty rotten, so the gobbing out procedure proved to be quite an easy task. Due to these bad, crumbly bricks, I had some level of concern, for when the pit-props would be burnt away and the chimney ready to collapse, what bothered me was the thought of it not falling over as planned but cork-screwing down into a bloody great heap of brickwork just like the deadly sod of a rotten stack that we encountered at Park Mill in Oldham several years ago. Real deadly stuff that can give you horrible nightmares.

Anyway with these terrible, crumbly bricks, mostly you didn't need the air-hammer to chisel out the gob. All you had to do was point the end of the chisel on one particular brick, press the trigger, and 'BANG' the brick just crumbled to dust. We could almost pick out the surrounding bricks with our bare hands, it were so easy. The problem were, once we'd removed a vertical line of bricks to form a slot for the 'pit-props', you had to carry out the task of placing the props and cap-pieces very carefully and then gingerly drive in the wooden wedges. This was because all of the bricks above were actually loose as well as thoroughly rotten. One belt wit t'hammer and they just turned to dust. Any road, me and Mick got the whole pit-propping job done in record time, and without bringing the monster towering pile of brickwork down on top of us. It were a good 'un like and I were reet chuffed."

Apparently on the day of the chimney drop, Monday 23rd November 1998, despite it being cold due to an icy wind, it was bright and relatively sunny with the sky pale blue. As Fred cheerily stated, *"just the right amount of breeze and sunshine for a Bolton chimney drop"*.

Fred and his assistants stacking the bonfire material in and around the supporting pit-props.
Mick Berry Collection

Fred clutches an old paint can filled with diesel fuel oil which he uses as an accelerant for the bonfire.
Mick Berry Collection

The Asia Mill chimney's demolition bonfire furiously burns. In the background Fred's trusty 'Lanny' is safely parked inside a shed, and further still the large crowd of Fred fans are gathered.
Mick Berry Collection

The massive gobbed out opening in the chimney base was beautifully supported on over twenty 'pit-props' and 'cap-pieces'. An eye-catching poignant slogan in white paint had been neatly painted above the gob: **THE END OF ASIA MILL CHIMNEY 23ʳᴰ NOVEMBER 1998.** Although Fred emphatically declared that it was not created by his own hand, and despite recalling seeing someone acting suspiciously around the chimney base, he conveniently couldn't remember the name of the 'artist' who was obviously adept at signwriting; I could however, discern by the twinkle in my old friend's eye, that this handywork was indeed the product of his masterly skill with an artist's horse-hair brush!

With about an hour to spare before the chimney's crematorial bonfire was to be lit at twelve noon, Fred and Mick commenced with the usual procedure of drilling numerous holes through the stout pit-props. Several other men were gathering a huge quantity of old demolition timber planking and car tyres from a mountainous pile which had been purposely stacked by the demolition contractor's men well away from the chimney base as a safeguard. This was good, time-proven practice, for on a number of other earlier chimney drops (Laburnum Mill, Atherton and Derwent Mill, Cockermouth, Cumbria),

vandals at these locations, on noticing that combustible materials forming the bonfire had been previously placed in position around the pit-props, had set fire to the materials which resulted in much anxiety and adverse publicity for Fred.

Following the completion of the pit-prop drilling exercise, Fred then instructed his eager assistants (demolition men and 'chimney buffs') to commence with the construction of the bonfire. At mid-day, bang on the nail, the bonfire was lit, and shortly after, gigantic orange flames leapt high in the air above the rapidly burning scrap timber and tyres, whilst the sky was darkened with the voluminous clouds of inky black smoke and clag that poured out of the chimney's top, some 160 feet above.

The sounds of the chimney's internal layers of rotten brickwork exploding and raining down the inside, and the roar of the fiery furnace, encouraged by the breeze filled the air. Fred and Mick Berry remained at their stations at the chimney bottom, keeping their eyes on the brickwork for the tell-tale crack that would inevitably appear once the 'pit-props' had been weakened by the fire. This crack would herald the chimney's collapse.

FRED DIBNAH'S CHIMNEY DROPS

At approximately 12.20 p.m., the crowd of watchers, who by now had grown to quite a considerable size, heard the distinctive sound of Fred's air-horn. The stricken chimney suddenly stirred, leaned over and commenced its fall along the planned drop zone, the bottom twenty feet cracking and disintegrating on its downward journey, and striking the mill yard with an almighty thunderous roar. Smoke and dust smothered the mill yard and also Fred's delighted audience, who were clapping, cheering, whistling and shouting their hero's praises.

Fred finished telling his story by saying, *"I were reet sad to see the Asia Mill chimney hit the deck. Especially as I had repaired it quite a few times, and it being one of the very last in Bolton".*

With massive cracks opening up in the brickwork, the chimney disintegrates and falls.
Mick Berry Collection

All that remains of the Asia Mill chimney is a lengthy, sinuous spread of broken bricks with smoke and steam rising to fill the air.
Mick Berry Collection

KIRKLEES MILL CHIMNEY DROP, BRANDLESHOLME, NR. BURY.

Sunday 28th April 2002

The 180 foot Kirklees Mill chimney rises sentinel-like above the old mill yard. A white plastic banner advertises WOODFORD INDUSTRIES LTD., the main demolition contractors.
©Alan McEwen Industrial Heritage Collection

Kirklees Mill which had once stood in the small valley or clough had during the winter of 2001-2 been totally demolished, leaving just the chimney standing sentinel-like. Woodford Industries Limited were the demolition specialists who had contracted Fred Dibnah to demolish the 180 foot, circular brick chimney.

Fred collected together his team of dedicated steeplejacks and chimney demolition men - old dependables like Mick Berry and Eddie Chattwood and these men spent the best part of a week 'gobbing out', propping and carrying out the usual procedures for demolishing a chimney - commencing on 15th April 2002.

FRED DIBNAH'S CHIMNEY DROPS

Fred and his team of helpers prepare the chimney's demolition by building a huge stack of scrap timber, which when lit will become the chimney's funeral pyre. Notice Fred's distinctive white paint gradation marks that denote the extent of the 'gobbing out' at the chimney's base. Fred's trusty Landrover is in the background.
©Alan McEwen Industrial Heritage Collection

The flat-topped knoll on the east side of the clough provided the perfect location for spectators and a large marquee was erected there for the various local personages - council officers and planning officials, developers and prospective customers who had all been invited to Fred's spectacular chimney demolition job by the main contractor.

I had been invited to attend and accompanying me was my fiancé Christine. This was her first meeting with Fred and therefore her very first chimney drop. On the morning of the chimney drop Sunday 28th April 2002, it was freezing with frequent showers of sleet and hailstones, Fred, Mick and Eddie and some of the site developer's men had commenced early that morning, putting the finishing touches to the chimney for the drop later that day. As Fred and his men were hard at work drilling the customary holes through the wooden pit-props, chiselling out a few more bricks from either side of the mouth opening, the

'gobbed out' section, and then gathering the scrap wood for the construction of the bonfire, over in the Great White Marquee, hundreds of bottles of wine and Guinness, casks of best bitter, plates stacked high with quality sandwiches and all manner of other goodies had been delivered and preparations were underway by the special catering company for the celebrations following the death of the Kirklees Mill chimney. The cost of the marquee and also the feast and drinks were provided by the Woodford specialist land reclamation company who had carried out the demolition of the mill buildings and the detoxification of the surrounding land - prior to the redevelopment of the whole of the valley bottom.

The chimney felling was scheduled for one o'clock on Sunday 28th April and from around mid-day the invited guests commenced arriving. Drinks were served and attractive public relations girls were to be seen promoting the company and chatting to some of the assembled guests.

Outside of the marquee a special viewing platform had been constructed which afforded an excellent view of the chimney located in the valley below, and many of the guests had set themselves up on this platform which had a bird's eye view. However, the weather was most unkindly; an extremely cold wind blew, gaining strength and then squalls of fine rain which quickly turned to sleet and hailstones the size of five pence pieces. Nevertheless, a number of brave souls, and my fiancé Christine and I weathered the storm and stayed put, despite us being drenched through and frozen. We could see Fred, Mick, Eddie and some other men struggling to complete the necessities prior to the lighting of the bonfire. The rain had turned the thick dust around the chimney base into a consistency somewhere between treacle and porridge! The men's boots and overalls below their knees were plastered in mud and filth.

My recollection is that due to the terrible weather conditions which had thoroughly soaked the wood for the chimney bonfire, the lighting of the fire was therefore delayed for around fifteen minutes. Looking down we could see Fred battling with the elements at the chimney base, wading through the glutinous mud that spread out in all directions, whilst attempting to light the improvised wooden shafted fire ignition torch. Then to make matters worse the wind velocity increased blowing down into the valley from the high Pennine moors beyond, and bringing with it heavy rain. Poor Fred, from our location on the viewing platform high on the top edge of the valley, his diminutive figure appeared bedraggled and half-drowned. Notwithstanding the ferocious weather, Fred being Fred bravely battled on and the bonfire was eventually lit and coaxed into life by one of the men at Fred's side, hurling a bucket of plant diesel onto the heaps of wet wood.

Fred later informed me, that due to the wind having changed direction just a short time before the planned chimney drop, he had considered abandoning the drop for safety reasons. His apparent concern was that the strong wind could cause the chimney to drop in the wrong direction. However, the chimney site being thoroughly cleared of any other structures and as there were no members of the public down in the mill yard, he eventually considered it safe for the demolition of the tall, brick stack to proceed.

Despite the wet wood, the fire soon burned ferociously, the massive tongues of flame being fanned by the strong wind, and thus within about 25 minutes from the ignition point, and in spite of the rain falling down from the leaden sky like machine gun bullets, I saw Fred gesticulate that the doomed, old brick stack was about to fall.

The flames have done their deadly work: the Kirklees Mill chimney topples, breaks its back and crashes to the ground accompanied by the resounding cheers, whistles and applause of the rain-drenched crowd of onlookers.
©Alan McEwen Industrial Heritage Collection

FRED DIBNAH'S CHIMNEY DROPS

The distinctive sound of his klaxon heralded the toppling of the chimney, and down the stack came, the barrel breaking into three sections. It struck the saturated surface of the mill yard with great violence, the shock wave reverberating up to where we stood on the hillside above.

Thereafter, the handful of thoroughly rain-soaked 'Fred fans' who had braved the elements on the hillside platform, following the usual cheering and applause for Fred and his team, trolleyed into the marquee where a most splendid celebration with much drink and food was in full swung. Christine and I entered the marquee where I introduced her to an old friend of Fred's, Owd Jake from Royton (now sadly deceased), whom despite his advancing years, (he was in his early 80s), he always came to the majority of the chimney drops to lend a hand stacking the bonfire material; always good humouredly and full of respect for Fred. Fred entered the marquee dripping wet and covered in mud.

"Hiya Alan, that were a reet worrying bugger. I didn't think it were going to fall due to the sodding wind", he exclaimed. *"Another one bites the dust ....very sad"*, he mournfully added. *"Where's me Guinness?"*, and off he sauntered towards the bar, a pool of muddy water following in his wake.

The aftermath: smoke and steam rises from the heaps of crushed brickwork. Another chimney expertly and safely brought down by Fred Dibnah.
©Alan McEwen Industrial Heritage Collection

The author in soaked-through guise, following the chimney demolition and just prior to recuperating with a pint of Guinness!
©Alan McEwen Industrial Heritage Collection

PARK NO. 2 MILL CHIMNEY DROP, ROYTON, OLDHAM.

Sunday 9th May 2004

Park No. 2 Mill Chimney on the morning of the demolition.
Gordon Connolly Collection

Ever since the early 1960s Fred Dibnah had been expertly felling mill and factory chimneys all over his own stamping grounds of Bolton, Rochdale, Oldham, Stockport, Warrington and many other former milltowns in the North West.

He occasionally travelled much further afield and particularly so when he became nationally famous resulting from the many successful and fascinating television programmes that featured his diverse talents and deep-seated interests in the world of industrial heritage, steam engines and his first love: steeplejacking. By early 2004, Fred had felled some 89 chimneys, many being highly complex to demolish, and profoundly dangerous.

Park No. 2 Mill chimney, approximately 195 feet tall and built in 1913 would be his 90th and sadly,

owing to his deteriorating health, his final chimney drop. Fred had been diagnosed in the autumn of 2001 with bladder cancer, but typical of this Northern milltown-born, hardworking and profoundly brave man, he cheerfully and stubbornly fought the disease until his untimely demise on the 6th November 2004.

Park No. 2 Mill was constructed as a six storey spinning mill of Accrington brick in 1913 by the Park & Sandylane Mill Company Limited and to the same layout as Park No. 1 Mill which dated back to 1875. In 1915 the spindleage amounted to 100,000, the spinning machines manufactured by Asa Lees. Park No. 2 Mill was powered by a 1600 horsepower steam engine built by Yates & Thom, of Blackburn; steam was generated in four Lancashire boilers. The impressive 195 foot tall circular chimney built of Accrington bricks provided the necessary draught to operate the Lancashire boilers. Owing to foreign competition and general unprofitability, the operating company closed down the mill in 1967. Shortly after, however, the Shiloh Group purchased the mill buildings and machinery and kept most of the machinery operating until 1977, when the curtain finally came down on cotton production. In 2003, the mill owner's sold the site for redevelopment and the whole mill was demolished leaving the chimney, which was in a dangerous condition, standing like the proverbial lone sentinel.

Fred's chimney drop was planned for one o'clock on Sunday the 9th of May and the Spring weather was kind to all concerned. Fred had gathered his trusty team around him, hard working, dependable old friends like Mick Berry from Bolton and fellow steeplejack Eddie Chattwood from Ramsbottom, who had worked with Fred since the 1960s. Both men were just like Fred, rough, tough characters, who had mountains of respect for Fred, and whose task it was to carry

out the majority of the back-breaking graft of 'gobbing out' the chimney base and supporting it by the 'pit-props'.

Fred and his men had originally planned to commence the chimney felling preparations on Monday the 2nd of May, but when they had arrived on site, to Fred's dismay, there was no compressor which was required to power the pneumatically operated air-hammers and drills. Ever resourceful, Fred then attempted to hire a compressor locally from one of the numerous plant hire firms in the Oldham area. However, due to it being May Day Bank Holiday, all plant hire companies were closed, so the team couldn't commence the cutting out of the chimney's brickwork until the next day, following the delivery to the site of a mobile, diesel compressor. Nevertheless, Fred was unconcerned, for he was totally confident that the team would have the chimney ready for demolition by the Sunday lunchtime.

Park and Sandy Mill Chimney standing a short distance from Park No. 2 Mill Chimney.
On the morning of the demolition of Park No. 2 Mill chimney Fred stated that he would drop Park and Sandy Mill Chimney next, but sadly this was not to be.
Gordon Connolly Collection

The two mill chimneys standing close together.
Gordon Connolly Collection.

Fred wearing with some reluctance, a green safety helmet, with fellow steeplejack Eddie Chattwood on the right and two contractors leaning on the Landrover.
Gordon Connolly Collection.

Fred's old and trusty workhorse, his 'Lanny'.
Gordon Connolly Collection.

Over the next few days, with Fred in command, Eddie and Mick plus one or two other 'chimney buffs' carried out the 'gobbing out' and 'pit-propping' procedure, to the ultimate satisfaction of Fred. On the Saturday morning, Fred and Eddie were working inside the base of the old chimney, completing some minor jobs, when suddenly a massive fall of damp congealed soot, which had been lodged high up in the chimney barrel, suddenly fell down and engulfed both steeplejacks. Both were fortunately unhurt. Upon crawling out, Fred comically exclaimed, his white eyes and white teeth lighting up his pitch-black face, *"Bloody hell, Eddie, I thought I'd lost you, we're as black as the ace of spades"*. They both roared with laughter.

Early on Sunday morning, the chimney drop day, Fred and his men were already on site. During the night, the demolition contractors had tipped an enormous load of firewood close to the base of the Park No. 2 Mill chimney in readiness for the building of the demolition pyre. Constables from Greater Manchester Police were to be observed, blocking off the surrounding streets of the former cotton town. Crowds of gaily dressed townsfolk gathered for the event. A Sky News van arrived with several reporters. Fred had become so nationally renown, that when he engineered the felling of a big factory chimney, it was guaranteed to appear on television screens all over Britain

which was excellent P.R. for the demolition contractors and site developers. The demolition contractors at the Park No. 2 Mill site had even erected a huge banner extending down the chimney's barrel to promote their name.

Overhead, the Greater Manchester Police helicopter was buzzing over the Park No. 2 Mill site like an angry bee, monitoring the burgeoning crowd, which was rumoured to be well over 2000 strong. About a couple of hours before the fire was lit, Fred received a complaint from a local council official who stated that an elderly man who lived in a white painted bungalow situated above Park Mill, was concerned that the vibration caused by Fred's dropping of the chimney would probably result in it causing serious damage to his collection of antiques. He had evidently complained to the council, and one of these officials had made it his duty to attend the Park No. 2 Mill site and address, not only the occupant of the white bungalow's concerns, but the council's too, and therefore, urged Fred to do his utmost to avoid creating an earth tremor!. After assuring the council man that everything would be alright, and the dropping of the chimney wouldn't cause an earthquake, Fred visited the elderly gentleman's bungalow to allay the occupant's fears and to view his antique collection.

A group of grimy chimney demo men (left to right) Mick Berry, Fred, Eddie Chattwood and Gordon Connolly with David Banks-Fear at the rear standing adjacent to the 'gobbed out' mouth at the chimney base.
Gordon Connolly Collection.

Mick Berry breaking out brickwork in the 'gob' with the powerful air operated drill which Fred had christened 'Big Bertha'.
Gordon Connolly Collection.

A close-up of the pneumatic drill 'Big Bertha'.
Gordon Connolly Collection

'Gobbed' opening or mouth cut into the chimney base and showing the 'pit-props'.
Gordon Connolly Collection.

Following his hasty visit to the white bungalow, Fred made his way back down the steeply sloping waste ground to the chimney. Mick Berry could see that his old friend Fred was obviously not feeling very well, due to his serious illness. As Fred met up with Mick he blurted out in an exasperated tone. *"I've got more antiques in my bloody toilet at home than he's got up there!"* The 'antiques' were apparently reproductions. Nevertheless, the elderly man had been assured by Fred that there wouldn't be a disaster, and he actually attended the chimney drop upon receiving a special invitation from the Master Steeplejack.

Fred's sons, Jack and Roger had come over from their home on the Isle of Man and were busily engaged around the chimney base assisting Mick, Eddie and several more willing assistants in the building of the bonfire and the other final preparations. Fred was clearly delighted but within the next couple of minutes he was suddenly surrounded with swarms of newspaper and television reporters, all of them attempting at once to interview the famous Boltonian steeplejack. In the streets surrounding Park No. 2 Mill amidst the mass of cheerful 'Fred fans' were numerous ice cream and hot-dog vans selling their refreshing and tasty products. All around, strangely attired men were to be seen clutching expensive cameras, and in the upstairs windows of the Coronation Street type terraced houses, Roytonian townsfolk could be seen with digital movie cameras mounted onto tripods.

By this time, a continuous stream of well-dressed, especially invited guests jostled around Fred, many seeking his autograph or shouting words of encouragement to their hero, others clicking away on digital cameras to capture the sight of the massive bonfire that was now stacked high and wide around the 'gobbed out' opening in the chimney base. With just a few minutes left before the lighting of the fire, Fred begun to move the mass of newspapermen, television broadcasters and the large throng of interested 'Fred fans', several hundred feet back to where it was considered safe to stand and watch.

Fred stands to the front of the partially built bonfire.
Gordon Connolly Collection.

Fred and Gordon building the bonfire.
Gordon Connolly Collection.

Improvised bonfire lighting torches.   Fred with bonfire ignition torch.
Gordon Connolly Collection

Fred and Sheila Dibnah stand with two of the demolition firm's representatives at the base of the chimney just prior to lighting.
Gordon Connolly Collection.

Sheila holds the torch as Fred prepares to light it .

Sheila lights the bonfire by inserting it into one of Fred's 'glory holes': a cache of highly flammable material.
Gordon Connolly Collection.

The chimney demolition bonfire erupts into massive flames that lick hungrily at the heaped combustible material.
Gordon Connolly Collection.

Enjoying their Sunday, some of the crowd of onlookers patiently await the death of the chimney.
Gordon Connolly Collection.

At one o'clock, bang on the nail, Fred could be seen instructing his attractive wife Sheila to set fire to the mountain of combustible material that formed the old Park No. 2 Mill chimney pyre. The fuel, which had been thoroughly soaked with numerous buckets of plant diesel oil, quickly commenced burning and soon, massive, long flames could be seen leaping high all around the bonfire. Several score yards away, the sound of the long sinuous, orangey-yellow flames being induced into the base of the chimney could be plainly heard, the fire roaring like the sound of a steam express train entering a tunnel. Enormous, long gouts of inky black smoke issued out of the stricken chimney's top to darken the sky above Royton. Within a wide arc surrounding the rear of the chimney, scores of cameras belonging to the television and newspaper photographers were all aimed on the fire-ravaged brick stack. Then,

exactly at 12.20 p.m. just as he had planned, Fred, who was standing at the rear of the chimney looking for a distinctive horizontal crack, the sure sign that the chimney was ready to fall, suddenly sounded his trusty klaxon and whilst looking up at the chimney to ensure the direction of its fall, he rapidly moved to a safe position. One, two, three seconds later and the chimney toppled to crash down exactly where Fred had engineered it to land. Amidst the shock wave of swirling dust, soot and smoke, a massive cheer burst from the thousands of people crammed all around the site. When the dust and smoke pall cleared, all that remained of the Park No.2 Mill chimney was just a long, narrow heap of slightly smoking brick rubble. The old man from the white bungalow on the hill above, the antique collector, was clearly satisfied and congratulated Fred.

A dramatic image of the chimney with smoke issuing from the top and the whole surrounding area wraithed in black smoke.
Gordon Connolly Collection.

The 'pit-props' have burnt away and the chimney commences its downward journey to earth.

...................and further still!

Gordon Connolly Collection.

Fred and Sheila Dibnah surrounded by his assistants, contractor's men and well-wishers stand atop the heap of still smoking brick rubble.
Gordon Connolly Collection.

PARK NO. 2 MILL, ROYTON, OLDHAM

This had been Fred Dibnah's final chimney drop, the end of an era and there was, for just a few moments after the dramatic chimney drop, an air of sadness pervading. Despite his ever-smiling facial expression, you could see the sadness in his eyes, *"Its all gone, done for"*, said Fred ever so sadly.

Master steeplejack Fred Dibnah's final chimney demolition; the end of an era.
Gordon Connolly Collection.

The celebration of the successful death of the Park Mill No. 2 Chimney gets under way at a local pub. From left: Mick Berry, Fred's son Roger Dibnah, Fred himself, Eddie Chattwood and Gordon Connolly.
Gordon Connolly Collection.

Six months later, and just four days before he died, whilst visiting Fred in the Bolton Hospice, he was lying on a bed and appeared to be asleep. I sat quietly down on a chair at the bedside, there was just myself and my old friend Fred, a devoutly brave man, a man who had inspired me and thousands more besides; a man unjustly stricken down by a dreadful terminal illness. After a few moments, as I rose from my chair to leave, Fred suddenly opened one of his eyes and he smiled in that very special, sunny way so peculiar to Fred, *"Hi Al, ar't awreet cock?",* he whispered in his distinctive Bolton accent. He then drifted back into a deep sleep. Sadly, it was indeed the end of a very special era.

THE END

For well over two decades my multi-talented friend Fred Dibnah was a deep source of inspiration to myself, and to be sure countless others. The interest and passion for Victorian mechanical and civil engineering and, may I say the virtues of earlier times, came over in Fred's many eloquent broadcasts on radio and television. Indeed, he breathed fresh air into the hitherto stuffy world of industrial history for the British people and he was universally loved and admired.

Gone, but never forgotten.

Your old friend Alan McEwen

Memorable images of Fred Dibnah's life from Alan McEwen's Industrial Heritage Collection.

The Impressive front aspect of Fred's former home, Park Cottage.
©Alan McEwen Industrial Heritage Collection

(Left) Close-up of the Earl of Bradford's arms which adorns Park Cottage.

(Right) The Blue Plaque was fitted to the front of Fred's former home, Park Cottage, 121 Radcliffe Road, Bolton, by Bolton Civic Trust.
©Alan McEwen Industrial Heritage Collection

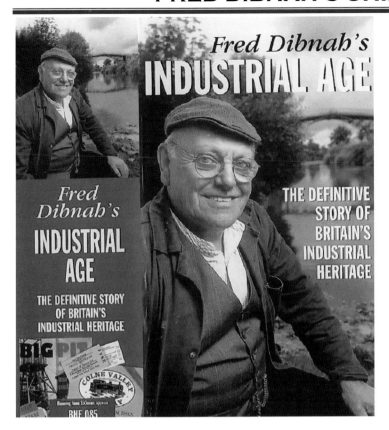

In 1999, Fred presented the author with a copy of 'Fred Dibnah's Industrial Age' which Fred had autographed in his usual distinctive style.
©*Alan McEwen Industrial Heritage Collection*

Standing alongside Fred's Aveling & Porter Steam Roller 'Betsy', at Chelford Traction Engine Rally, Cheshire, Fred and the author swap yarns about 'old boilers, steam engines and chimney demolition exploits'. All good stuff, and now sadly missed!
©*Alan McEwen Industrial Heritage Collection*

The author's signed copy of Don Haworth's 'The Fred Dibnah Story' – autographed in Fred's beautiful copperplate – which he proudly presented to me in his hen hut workshop, during one of our regular chats on a dark November evening in 1993.

©Alan McEwen Industrial Heritage Collection.

Fred presented the author with this autographed image of his dare-devil pose atop the steeple of St. Walburgh's Church, Preston, the third tallest spire in England at 300 feet.

Fred and the author at Atlas No. 4 Mill, 20th October 1992
Eddie Chattwood Collection

Fred's distinctive Compliments Slip

Fred and the author standing in the front of the shed with Fred's beloved Aveling & Porter steam tractor at the rear, June 2004.
©Alan McEwen Industrial Heritage Collection

Fred's Aveling & Porter steam roller, Betsy, at Abbotsfield Park, Flixton, Manchester. May 1994.
©Alan McEwen Industrial Heritage Collection

The ornate brick chimney was built by Fred when aged 17 in 1955 and adorns his parents'
'Coronation Street' style house, on Alfred Street, off Manchester Road, Bolton.
©Alan McEwen Industrial Heritage Collection

Street Sign ALFRED STREET.
©Alan McEwen Industrial Heritage Collection

The author stands in front of Fred Dibnah's statue cast from bronze, the week following the unveiling of the statue in Oxford Street, Bolton on 29th April 2008. The date was specifically chosen, as it would have been Fred's 70th birthday. To the rear is the vertical inverted mill steam engine built by famous Bolton engineers, Hick, Hargreaves and fondly revered by Fred.
©Alan McEwen Industrial Heritage Collection

Close-up study of Fred's face in bronze.
©Alan McEwen Industrial Heritage Collection

Fred's grave in Tonge Cemetery, Bolton.
The distinctive headstone is made from sandstone and Welsh slate, the inscribed words are picked out in gold leaf. The letter 'b' in the word 'remember', forms a tall factory chimney with wreaths of smoke curling out. Significant and poignant.
Sheila, Fred's wife placed a great deal of thought regarding the choosing of the materials for Fred's headstone and moreover for the magnificent design.
Fred undoubtedly was a national treasure.
'A Much Loved Steeplejack'
©Alan McEwen Industrial Heritage Collection

H.A. McEwen (Boiler Repairs) Ltd

Established 1968
Boilermakers – Boiler Repair Specialists – Boiler Plant Engineers

Telephone: 01535 634674   Fax: 01535 636802
Email: enquiries@mcbo.co.uk
www.mcbo.co.uk
Alasdair McEwen - Mob. 07799 426108

Proudly serving British Industry and the Heritage World for over 40 years.

McEwen's supplied this 18,000 lbs/hour twin furnace, coal-fired package boiler and carried out the full installation to a West Yorkshire textile company.

McEwen's specialise in heavy structural boiler repairs, coded welding to BS 287 and BS 288, overhauling of steam valves, steam plant installation and repairs and finally all types of fabrication work.

Highly specialised re-tubing of Robey packaged steam boiler at Blackburn Hospital.

Structural repairs to combustion chamber of Babcock boiler.

Annual preparation for inspection of large packaged steam boiler.

Flanged steel backhead for locomotive 62005. All types of flanged throat plates, tube plates, firebox endplates, dished and flanged ends a speciality.

New flanged and all-welded locomotive fireboxes, smoke boxes and ash pans.

New riveted traction engine fireboxes and tube plates.

Design and construction of all types of steam boat boilers, model traction engine and locomotive boilers a speciality.

New title to be published in late 2009 by Sledgehammer Engineering Press Limited.

The author, Christine McEwen's beautiful and evocative images in full colour of historic packhorse bridges to be found all over Northern England together with 'potted histories' of each individual bridge.

JAGGERMEN'S BRIDGES ON PACKHORSE TRAILS

Christine McEwen

SLEDGEHAMMER ENGINEERING PRESS LIMITED